The Impulsive Character

THE IMPULSIVE CHARACTER
and other writings

by
Wilhelm Reich

TRANSLATED BY
Barbara G. Koopman

A MERIDIAN BOOK
NEW AMERICAN LIBRARY
TIMES MIRROR

MERIDIAN TRADEMARK REG. U.S. PAT. OFF. AND FOREIGN COUNTRIES
REGISTERED TRADEMARK—MARCA REGISTRADA
HECHO EN CHICAGO, U.S.A.

SIGNET, SIGNET CLASSICS, MENTOR, PLUME and
MERIDIAN BOOKS
are published by The New American Library, Inc.,
1301 Avenue of the Americas, New York, New York 10019
First Printing, October, 1974
1 2 3 4 5 6 7 8 9
PRINTED IN THE UNITED STATES OF AMERICA

To Elsworth Baker

"The articles by Wilhelm Reich which comprise this work first appeared in English translation in the *Journal of Orgonomy*. In addition to samplings of Dr. Reich's work, this publication offers a wide range of articles in the field of Orgonomy, and draws its contributors from such diversified disciplines as Orgone Therapy, Physics, Social Science and Education. Recent contributors have included Dr. Elsworth F. Baker, A.S. Neill and Dr. Ola Raknes. Interested readers may order the *Journal of Orgonomy* by writing:

Orgonomic Publications, Inc
P.O. Box 476
Ansonia Station
New York, New York 10023

Contents

─────────────

Foreword

This is the first publication in book form, in English, of some of Wilhelm Reich's early writings. The book is divided into two parts. The first, consisting of the monograph *The Impulsive Character,* originally published in 1925, is purely psychoanalytical and was written during the author's years in Freud's Psychoanalytic Polyclinic in Vienna. The second part, written considerably later, finds Reich deeply involved in biophysics and consists of three important articles that laid the foundation for medical orgonomy. Arranged chronologically, they are: "The Basic Antithesis of Vegetative Life Functions" (written in 1934), "The Orgasm as an Electrophysiological Discharge" (also written in 1934), and "Experimental Investigation of the Electrical Function of Sexuality and Anxiety" (written in 1936 and first published in 1937). These articles, milestones in the history of orgonomy, show the development of Reich's thinking and research from psychoanalysis through his discoveries of vegetative functioning and armoring to orgone energy. One is constantly amazed at his early insights and his ability to plumb the basic issues in both healthy and neurotic functioning. He always thought in functional terms and never allowed himself to indulge in psychoanalytic psychologizing.

The Impulsive Character was written when Reich was only three years out of medical school, but even at this early date he emphasizes the importance of character analysis over the then prevailing free association method. In this monograph he deals with the dynamics of the poorly understood impulsive, or psychopath, and compares the development of this character with normal development and the development of the impulse-inhibited character, or common neurotic. His findings are still valid, though he subsequently changed some of the views that

hen with his contemporaries. For example, in this
he believes that a well-developed latency period
y for the achievement of sublimation and thus health.
He points out that the impulsive with his chaotic behavior
and inability to sublimate has a very short latency period or
none at all. But Bronislaw Malinowski showed that the Trobriand Islanders, who were sex-affirmative and allowed children peer-related sexual activity, had no latency period. If
the oedipal conflict is decathected in childhood through such
activity, there is no need for sexual repression in the latency
period. Thus latency is a cultural and not a natural phenomenon. Reich came to fully accept Malinowski's findings.

A second instance in which he was to radically change his
view was on the subject of infant feeding. At this time he
took for granted the notion that infants must learn to nurse
at scheduled intervals. He later saw that this was a compulsive
attitude and felt that the infant should be allowed to regulate
its own schedule, not only in eating but also in all its other
natural needs. Thus developed his concept of self-regulation.

Little had been written on the impulsive up to that time.
Such cases did not turn up in private practice, and whatever
was known had been derived from observation in psychiatric
hospitals. The Psychoanalytic Polyclinic was established by
Freud for the treatment of the poor. Here Reich saw and treated
many such cases analytically, and this allowed him to arrive
at a number of conclusions about their development. Invariably
their upbringing combined a total lack of supervision with the
unbridled discharge of impulse, together with periods of a suddenly imposed repressive training, cruel and sadistic in nature,
by parents or other adults. This meant that many impulses
broke through in their original form, side by side with the
repressed id strivings—this latter giving rise to such neurotic
manifestations as compulsions, phobias, and amnesias.

All of these patients had been exposed to a chaotic and
usually brutal sexual life, beginning at the age of four or even
earlier and often involving rape by fathers or other adults and
indiscriminate sexual play with other children. The child was

unable to handle this situation emotionally, as compared to the voluntary, gentle peer-sexuality of the Trobriand Islanders. Sexuality thus remained infantile in character, largely polymorphous perverse and incapable of providing discharge of stasis, which was thus severe in all cases. These impulsives lived out their sexuality very early and with conscious incest wishes. Sadomasochistic behavior was routine. Many of the characteristics of schizophrenia were present, and in some cases it was difficult to differentiate between the two.

Reich found that the impulsive had no circumscribed fixation point such as one finds in the usual neurotic. Actually all erogenous zones were early and equally active, and it was impossible to ascribe any specific fixations. The ego was markedly narcissistic and suggested the schizophrenic. It remained polarized between pleasure ego and superego and defended itself not only against the id in the service of the superego, but also against the superego in the service of the id. This gave rise to the overriding disorganization of the impulsive character. The problem would seem to be a defect in the superego in which repression is dynamic and therefore unsuccessful. Reich coined the term "isolated" for this situation: the superego is not incorporated into the ego and systematic repression is lacking.

Ambivalence is always present, but there are no reactive formations such as one finds in the usual neurotic. Guilt is also present but remains unattached to the impulses which are allowed expression, such as sadistic acts or criminal behavior. Rather, it is prominent in those areas where repression occurs. Reich achieved considerable success with these individuals and grew to appreciate them for the degree of life they showed, however grossly distorted it might be. He found them more likable than the usual impulse-inhibited neurotic.

This monograph is particularly important and appropriate at this time for an understanding of the present notable increase in openly impulsive behavior among college students and young militants. This seems to be a result of the contactless permissiveness and unsupervised upbringing so prevalent during the past twenty years: the child, deprived of direction or guidance, feels unloved and cannot establish his ego boundaries. The result is a chaotic libido economy, giving rise to unbearable tension in a structure incapable of normal discharge.

Even in 1925, Reich, with his keen perception, questioned the sex-negative attitude of the times toward children and felt that they should be allowed their own sexual expression according to their age and developmental level, and that this should be affirmed and protected by society. He was to feel this more and more strongly as time passed. At the same time he deplored contactless permissiveness, which he regarded as license rather than freedom.

In the three shorter essays in this book, Reich essentially effected a departure from psychoanalysis into the realm of sex economy and biophysics. In the first paper, "The Basic Antithesis of the Vegetative Life Functions," his functional thinking took him logically and inevitably from the psychic to the physiological realm. Here he starts with the observation that the affect of anxiety, a psychic phenomenon, has a somatic counterpart in the vegetative nervous system. From this he derives a common law, energetically based, governing both the psyche and the soma—namely, the functional identity and antithesis of sexuality and anxiety.

Sexuality then becomes movement out toward the world, or parasympathetic expansion; and anxiety becomes movement away from the world, or sympathetic contraction. Reich thus solved a problem that had long puzzled physiologists. Why does the parasympathetic, for example, contract the bladder and relax the sphincter while the sympathetic relaxes the bladder and contracts the sphincter? The same is true in the intestinal tract. It seemed paradoxical that one part of the vegetative system should at the same time contract one muscle and relax another, and vice versa. Reich clearly shows why when he demonstrates that the parasympathetic produces expansion, or movement toward the world, and the sympathetic produces contraction, or movement away from the world—*from the standpoint of the total organism*. One comes to understand that muscular armoring is simply a specific chronic sympathetic excitation (anxiety) which prevents the organism from moving out toward the world and particularly from expressing destructive aggression (hate).

Reich points out that previous investigators had erred in trying to find a meaning in physiological functions. Basic physiological functions cannot in themselves be interpreted psychologically; only their disturbances can be psychogenic. The psychic apparatus has grown out of the biophysical one, and thus certain laws pertaining to the latter must also govern the former—such as tension, discharge, stimulus, response, and so on. On the other hand, certain laws apply only to the psychic and are therefore antithetical to the physiological—such as the repression of instinctual drives, introjection, projection, identification, and so on.

Reich also makes the interesting observation that the muscular system, the apparatus of destruction, has its origin in the mesoderm, a secondary embryonic structure, while the apparatus of the sexual and anxiety functions is already present in the protozoon. One may recall in this regard that protozoa do not die naturally but merely divide.

Reich foresees muscular armoring by noting that living organisms tend to assume a spherical shape when threatened. In other words, they contract. In the higher animals, where muscles are present, this contraction takes place largely in the muscular system.

The second paper in this series, "The Orgasm as an Electrophysiological Discharge," marks a further advance into biophysics. Here Reich clearly recognizes an energy discharge in the orgasm, but has not yet identified it as orgone energy. Understandably he sees it as an electrical discharge. He accordingly defines the orgasm formula as mechanical tension, electrical charge, electrical discharge, and mechanical relaxation, and he asks whether the orgasm is a function to be found throughout living nature. This he was later able to verify.

Each partner in the sexual act forms part of an electrical system consisting of (1) male circulation; (2) male boundary layer (penile epidermis); (3) female secretions (conducting medium); (4) female boundary (vaginal mucosa); (5) female circulation. The acid vaginal secretion, which is an electrolyte, represents the contact medium between the penile epidermis and vaginal mucosa. The male and female circulations and the mutually stimulating plasmatic excitations in the autonomic nervous system represent the inherent sources of electrical charge on the organs of contact. Equalization of the potential gradient occurs between the two surfaces—penile epidermis and vaginal mucosa. We now know that the energy involved is not electrical in nature—Reich later called it "orgone energy" and viewed the organism as a total orgone energy system.

In the light of these findings, the present writer has described the sexual act as follows:

> As energy increases, the body regularly builds up tension. At a certain point, known as the lumination point, the tension is felt as sexual excitement in the healthy individual. Then normal expansion markedly increases. The skin becomes warm and dry, the pulse full and slow, breathing is deep, vision is sharp, and the genitals fill with blood and become acutely sensitive. The orgone energy field expands and is highly charged. In full sexual excitement, not only must energy reach the skin surface, particularly the genitals, but this energy must be excited from the core. For excitation to come from the core (the vegetative system), acceptance of the genital feeling and anticipation of the genital embrace are necessary. Excitation is further increased through the field and membrane of the sexual object until close contact and union of the genitals become imperative. Rhythmic friction with the medium of a mucus vaginal secretion rapidly produces a peak of energy concentration and excitation in the genital. Discharge occurs through total convulsions of the body—the orgasm—and the economic energy level is reestablished.[1]

The third paper, "Experimental Investigation of the Electrical Function of Sexuality and Anxiety," is an extremely important and brilliant essay that sets forth the experimental evidence on which Reich based the conclusions he drew from his therapeutic work with patients. Biophysics here emerges as a natural science. This was the first time in the annals of science that a subjective experience had been quantified by objective measurements. Freud's concept of the libido is shown conclusively to be a real energy. The basic antithesis of pleasure (outward toward the world) and anxiety (withdrawal from the world) is shown in the rise or fall of "electrical" charge at the skin surface according to pleasurable or painful stimuli, with the charge corresponding exactly to the sensations felt by the subject being tested. Though all areas of the skin have essentially .the same charge in the resting state, erogenous areas have a much greater reactivity to pleasure or pain, and after a disappointment or traumatic experience, reaction to pleasure is slow and cautious. Also, a repeated stimulus does not produce so great an effect as an initial one, and this helps to explain why people who are together too often lose their ability to excite each other.

These experiments also clarify healthy and neurotic sexual behavior. For example, an erect penis shows little increase in charge unless pleasure is felt in the erection. Mechanical tumescence alone cannot increase the charge. Pleasure cannot be forced or achieved voluntarily, but only if the individual is ready for it emotionally. The highest charge is produced by gentle friction in the sequence of an initial withdrawal followed by a forward thrust. It is similar to an animal pulling back before making a spring. One can thus see the rationale of natural movements in the genital embrace.

The centers of biological excitation reside in the vegetative nervous system and lie beyond conscious control. It is therefore futile to seek an intellectual understanding of one's problems unless the body is freed of its unconscious holding and can again function spontaneously in accordance with natural law.

We are indebted to Dr. Barbara Koopman for making these pivotal works available in English and for the clarity, skill, and fidelity of her translation.

ELSWORTH F. BAKER, M.D.

Translator's Preface

Now that the concepts of vaginal orgasm and genital primacy are under fire from many quarters, including such researchers as Masters and Johnson, it is especially timely that Reich's experiments in sexuality should appear in English translation. Though they predate the above investigations by decades, they offer a far deeper understanding of the mysteries of orgastic functioning. Here Reich signals the cardinal importance of genital orgasm as a regulator of the total energy economy. His view represents a far broader concept than that of local climaxes fired off from various erogenous zones. To Masters and Johnson, if I understand them rightly, an orgasm is an orgasm no matter what triggers it, and therefore vaginal orgasm is of no special importance for sexual health. They fail to distinguish between a local climax (partial discharge) and the total bodily convulsions of genital orgasm as described by Reich. It is only the latter that can fully discharge the sexual tension accumulated in the living organism. (Partial discharge of tension only begets more tension. The differential between energy buildup and energy discharge provides the somatic core of the neuroses.) Not even multiple consecutive climaxes can accomplish this libidinal-economic task.

The thinking that culminated in the monumental *Function of the Orgasm* of 1942 is already present in the early biological papers translated here. According to Reich, the orgasm is, physiologically speaking, far more than a mechanical filling and emptying of fluids. It also entails a process of bioelectric charge and discharge and is therefore a paradigm of all life functions, such as the beating of the heart, wherein mechanical filling and emptying in systole and diastole is accompanied by a buildup and ebbing of bioelectric energy (as manifested in the electrocardiogram).

oned that mechanical tumescence and detumes-
adequately explain orgastic phenomena, since
ulation, and detumescence can occur without any
~~~~~ ~~ ~~~~~~action or may even evoke displeasure and disgust.
For satisfaction to ensue, he postulated, there must be a bioenergetic charging and discharging of the sexual apparatus and
of the total organism, in addition to the mechanical accumulation and ebbing of body fluids.

In a long series of carefully controlled experiments (published
herewith) he was able to corroborate this hypothesis. He first
established that both erogenous and nonerogenous skin sites
served as loci for the buildup of bioelectric potential, with
the erogenous zones showing a much wider range in both buildup capacity and loss of charge. Subjects connected to an oscill-
lograph regularly showed a sharp upward deflection when an
erogenous zone was stimulated, but *only if* subjective feelings
of pleasure were experienced. If an identical stimulus on the
same subject evoked displeasure or annoyance, there was a
sharp *downward* deflection of the graph, corresponding to a
sharp decrease in bioelectric charge (withdrawal of charge from
the skin surface). For example, an erect penis produced no
upward deflection of the graph unless pleasurable excitation
was felt by the subject. The oscillographic reading always
reflected accurately the *amount* of pleasure experienced. Thus
a *subjective* experience of pleasure was *objectively* quantified
by the instrument and coincided with a demonstrable buildup
in bioelectric potential. This bioelectric energy behaved differently from electromagnetism and was considered by Reich to
be functionally identical to Freud's "libidinal energy"—now
no longer a Freudian metaphor but an empirically demonstrable
energy, which he later termed "orgone."[1]

The same biophysical energy was reflected as *pleasure* if
it flowed *outward* to the skin surface, with resultant buildup
of charge at the skin site; as *anxiety* if it flowed *away* from
the skin surface, causing a lowering of charge at the skin site
and increased central (visceral) tension. In higher organisms,
the autonomic nervous system mediates this expansion and
contraction; in lower life forms, organic and inorganic chemical

substances subserve this vital pulsatory function.

These experiments show conclusively the basic antithesis of sexuality and anxiety. Energy flowing from center to periphery is functionally identical to pleasure; energy flowing from periphery to center is functionally identical to anxiety. It is the *direction of flow* of this energy that determines the one or the other.

The capacity to experience genital orgasm with full bioenergetic (orgonotic) charge and discharge entails plasmatic motility of the organism—that is, an absence of armoring. which is the somatic counterpart of psychic conflicts. (Reich likened the armored body to an undulating serpent that had been tied down in many places with consequent compromise to its motility.) Reich's view is functional rather than dualistic: psyche and soma are two sides of the same coin and share as their common functioning principle orgone energy functions. Therefore, orgonomic psychiatry concomitantly treats both character structure (psychic aspect) and physical armoring (somatic aspect). Success or failure depends largely upon the patient's capacity to overcome energy stasis and tolerate the higher excitation of his organism consequent to the unblocking of the energy flow.

The Impulsive Character also makes a timely appearance on the contemporary scene. It is my feeling that the practicing psychiatrist of today may be witnessing a new breed of patient in the making—a transitional form between the impulse-inhibited neurotic and the impulse-driven psychopath.

In today's setting of apparent sexual "freedom," old restraints are coming loose, but the underlying structure now evolving is far from genitality. Armored parents tend to distort the meaning of self-regulation and to go to extremes of permissiveness, inconsistency, or abdication in their child-rearing practices. They may parade naked in front of their children and condone pornography as harmless, then wonder how they have failed as "enlightened" parents. This is a far cry from the sexual freedom that Reich had in mind. It is merely the opposite pole of sexual repression—license.

Such contactless upbringing makes for libidinal chaos in the offspring. The old sexual repression is gone, and the individual cannot fall back on it as a means of binding his anxiety; his underlying ego structure remains infantile and narcissistic. Without the capacity for proper object relations, he cannot adequately discharge his sexual tension. All attempts to do so generate more pressure than they dispel. Instead of serious sexual commitment, sleeping with someone has become as casual as sharing a beer. Instead of the capacity for release that comes with genital primacy, there is a never-ending tension that drives the frantic organism to seek peace at any price—in the solace of drugs or through violent discharge in the social arena. Because of their intense inner discomfort, the young hate their nurturers, who indeed share a large burden of responsibility for this internal maelstrom. Such hatred is often projected as a hatred of the fatherland, and the child, in his suffering, identifies with the underdog.

Herein lies the long-range danger. The child has been reared with the tantalizing illusion of freedom but suffers an intolerable tension that he cannot comprehend. He is therefore driven to quiet the turmoil within himself, often by aligning himself with causes that freeze all movement from without. This is the essence of what Reich called the "emotional plague"—the need to still the movement of energy at every level, to freeze everything into a monolithic society where even mobility of thought is taboo. Such a youngster falls ready prey to the disciplined totalitarian who, for his own ulterior motives, preaches social justice and relief of the oppressed. Or he may turn to drugs to quell the turmoil—everything from marijuana to hard narcotics—thereby slamming the brakes on his disordered energy system.

The troubled youngster of today, with his disordered libidinal organization and unbearable inner tensions, bears considerable kinship to the impulsive of 1925 and indeed becomes much more comprehensible in the light of Reich's trail-blazing monograph.

At the outset, Reich incorporated many Freudian concepts into his thinking, including the theories of psychosexual development and libido-economics. As the reader will recall, the latter postulates that every individual at birth is endowed with a given quantum of psychic energy. The vicissitudes of this energy, through various phases of psychosexual development, determine the character and fate of the individual. The more energy that is bound up in regression and fixation at early developmental phases, the less there is available for autonomous adult functioning. To Freud, "psychic energy" was a metaphor, while to Reich it had a physical, objective existence, which he was able to demonstrate experimentally. Reich reasoned that for a person to maintain health he must have an orderly energy metabolism entailing periodic discharge through genital orgasm. In the absence of this, libidinal energy (not "sexual substances") becomes dammed up in the organism (stasis) and constitutes the somatic core of the neurosis (analogous but not identical with Freud's concept of "actual neurosis"). Reich saw sexual repression as the main cause of this stasis.

It is on this issue of sexual repression that Reich and Freud first part company. It is also the issue that has chiefly given rise to the distortions and misinterpretations of Reich. Whereas classical psychoanalysis saw the child as an impulse-dominated beast who must be tamed through sexual repression (frustration of the incest wish), Reich felt that sexual repression was at the root of man's illness. He advocated the acceptance of childhood sexuality (at an age-appropriate level) and pointed out that the discharge of sexual energy with peers would divest the incest wish of its libidinal charge. With decathexis of this wish, there would be no need to repress it. It should be clearly understood that Reich never advocated sexual relations between adults and children, the acting out of incest, the parental masturbation of children, or the salacious promotion of childhood sexual activity. Rather, his concept of self-regulation meant the noninterference with, as well as the protection of, peer-related childhood sexuality as part of the natural life functioning of the child.

As for the technical details of translation, I have tried to offer a faithful rendering of the original. It is an enlightening experience to trace Reich's thinking in German, step by step, from his origins in psychoanalysis to his breakthrough into psychobiology and the ultimate discovery of life energy functions.

The footnotes, with rare exceptions, are Reich's, as they appear in the original text. I have chosen to leave his bibliographical references in German, except for a few well-known works, such as *The Ego and the Id*. Occasional words or phrases, not in the original text, have been added in brackets for greater clarity of translation.

I should like to express thanks to the following for their help in problems of syntax and vocabulary: Hella Freud Bernays, Joseph Gross, M.D., and W. C. Britz; and to Norman M. Levy, M.D., for patient rereadings, corrections, and suggestions.

BARBARA GOLDENBERG KOOPMAN, M.D., Ph.D.

The Impulsive Cha____ _.

1. Introduction

We are, at the present time, without a single systematic theory of character rooted in psychoanalysis. Basically, psychoanalytic research focuses first on isolated phenomena and only later synthesizes the separate findings into an overall working hypothesis. This approach applies to the individual analysis, as well as to the broader realm of psychopathology. To evolve a psychoanalytic theory of character, we must know the exact mechanisms of psychic development, down to the finest detail. We are still a far cry from fulfilling this requirement.

The theory of psychosexual development appears sound in its basic aspects, yet it still does not go far enough toward achieving a characterological interpretation of personality. Those who are thoroughly familiar with psychoanalytic developments and Freud's key works on the subject—those who, in the dual role of analyst and analysand, "caught on" fast to the analytic experience—will also grasp that ego dynamics are far harder to formulate than id dynamics.

As Freud has repeatedly stressed in his basic works, recently in *The Ego and the Id*,[1] psychoanalysis has zealously avoided dealing with psychopathology by resorting to ready-made, constructive theories. Since analysis focused mainly on a genetic interpretation—on a "psychic embryology," so to speak—it had to take the longer and harder route of detailed probing, which surely had an impact on the therapeutic process. For the analyst must first recognize and understand developmental defects and then use this knowledge to modify them wherever possible. For this reason, psychoanalysis is presently as incom-

*Translated from *Der triebhafte Charakter*, International Psychoanalytic Press, 1925.

1

plete as its theory. The ideal theoretic basis of analytic therapy would be the complete genetic understanding of the patient's character.

Psychoanalysis stopped being symptomatic treatment a long time ago; rather, more and more it is becoming a therapy of character. We can trace this change to Freud's first awareness that the essence of analytic work does not lie in guessing a symptom's unconscious meaning and sharing it with the patient, but in the recognition and removal of resistances.[2] In resistance, two basic elements regularly find expression: first, every resistance contains repressed material relating to the specific analytic situation; and at the same time it contains the repressing mechanism, which constitutes the defense. Second, in addition to these specific components, or rather in addition to the content, a special form of resistance exists. Every resistance takes its specific character from the total personality structure, so to speak. The defense against an incestuously based transference resistance has the same content in a compulsive as it does in an hysteric, but an altogether different form—namely, the compulsive or hysterical character structure, respectively. An understanding of content suffices for the most probing analytic work; to note how the patient's character reveals itself in resistances is not so meaningful at first. Yet, if we go beyond thinking in terms of mere symptom analysis, we realize the following: the most important consideration is not the removal of symptoms but the substrate of the neurotic reactions—that is, the neurotic character structure itself. If we wish to render the patient incapable of regression—in other words, effect a real cure—we must replace symptom analysis with character analysis. But it is only recently that character analysis has gained prominence in analytic work. It did not happen *expressis verbis*.[3] Ferenczi and Rank[4] point up the importance of analyzing neurotic behavior and are critical of the main approach now in use, that of analyzing the symptom or the complex; rather, they stress the need for dealing with the patient primarily in terms of his actions. However, this creates the impression that they are neglecting the memory work, which Freud always put first in the therapeutic endeavor. But it is certainly in the analysis of neurotic behavior that character analysis gets its greatest leverage, far more so than in "memory analysis." This is because the sum total of character attitudes and traits unfolds most vividly in behavioral manifestations. Yet analysis of behavior must lead to recollection and to analytic reconstruction of the sources of behavior if we are to derive an adequate understanding of its genesis. On the other hand, experience has taught us that patients who do not act out tend to be untouched by therapy, despite deep-reaching memory work.

Fragments of a psychoanalytic characterology first appeared in Freud's study of the anal erotic character,[5] a theme greatly expanded by Jones[6] and Abraham[7] in particular. Here, for the first time, Freud signaled the role played by drives in the formation of specific character traits: frugality, orderliness, pedantry, cleanliness, obstinacy, and so on—these he recognized as direct, rather than neurotic, derivatives of the anal erotic character. We have yet to explain how an instinctual drive gets discharged in one patient through a neurotic symptom and in another through a character trait. In a similar vein, urethral erotic drives sometimes give rise to neurotic symptoms like premature ejaculation (Abraham) and nocturnal enuresis (Freud, Sadger, Stekel), and at other times to such traits as envy, which is a specific character trait, not a symptom.

The same applies to the role of sadism in the compulsive character, a type far easier to see through characterologically than is the hysteric, for example. It is also difficult to explain why, in some patients, that universal phenomenon, "repetition compulsion,"[8] predominates as a character trait (in the form of a compulsion to experience a given situation over and over again), while in other patients it does not seem to play the role assigned to it by its biological nature. There are neurotic characters without neurotic symptoms; there is symptom neurosis without character formation, in which the total personality is essentially pathological. All these problems belong in the realm of a psychoanalytic characterology—its basic methodology must evolve a comparative analytic psychology, analogous to the development of a comparative embryology.

The medical analyst may take great intellectual satisfaction in interpreting symptoms, tracing the sources of various character traits, and practicing causal therapy; but he should never fool himself about the need for a systematic theory of character, a lack more sorely felt as clinical experience has begun to signal the overriding importance of character analysis.

In Freud's *The Ego and the Id,* we find the groundwork

for a psychoanalytically based theory of character. The process of identification holds the key to the characterological interpretation of personality:

> The character of the ego is a precipitate of abandoned object cathexis. . . . Since then, we have come to understand that this kind of substitution has a great share in determining the form taken on by the ego and that it contributes materially towards building what is called character.[9]

This important developmental process may also take a pathological turn:

> If they obtain the upper hand and become too numerous, unduly powerful and incompatible with one another, a pathological outcome will not be far off. It may come to a disruption of the ego in consequence of the different identifications becoming cut off from one another by resistances; perhaps the secret of the cases of what is described as "multiple personality" is that the different identifications seize hold of consciousness in turn. Even when things do not go so far as this, there remains the question of conflicts between the various identifications into which the ego comes apart, conflicts which cannot after all be described as entirely pathological.[10]

Freud then makes the following distinction between ego and superego: the superego actually represents a replacement of object choices; the ego, on the one hand, subordinates itself to the superego and, on the other, offers itself as a love object to the superego, just as it once behaved toward the parents. But the superego is "two-faced," for it contains not only the enjoinder, "You must be like your father," but also the injunction, "You must not be like your father; that is, you may not do everything he does, since many things are reserved for him." Thus Freud has provided a frame of reference for further detailed work. Specifically, in *The Ego and the Id*, he has left open the question of the role played by erogenous zones in the formation of the ego ideal. A closely allied problem is the relationship of the specific erogenous zone to the object choice. The following factors must surely be of utmost significance in the formation of character, both normal and pathological:

1. Those aspects of the parents' personalities incorporated by the child into a positive or negative ego ideal.
2. Whether the boy's ego ideal followed the father or mother pattern (the same applies to the girl), and how that model

for the ego ideal was actually constituted.

3. And, also important, the stage of libidinal development at which an effective identification takes place. In the chronological interaction of sexual development and ego formation, the specific determinants of character formation must be sought[11] (for example, an effective identification in the genital or anal phase).

4. Also unknown to us are the conditions under which the ego ideal sets up its demands; for there is not only a reality ego, which is the sum total of all the ego ideal demands the "so be it," as it were; but also a whole series of unrealized ego ideal demands, the "so must it be." And we know that the tension between the "so be it" (reality ego) and the "it must or must not be" (superego) is at the root of many an illness.

5. Finally, we must consider that a primitive pleasure ego exists long before any identification and that its attitude toward identifications plays a decisive role in their outcome.

Though the problems briefly sketched here stem from the characterological aspect of every analysis, to inch toward a resolution (even in a mild transference neurosis) is fraught with great difficulty. This is especially true of those patients showing gross defects in their ego structure; such individuals are in constant conflict with the outside world and behave as if they had never advanced beyond the first stages of identification or superego formation. There are certain neurotics who are subject to a typical form of repetition compulsion: the asocial types, the occasional criminal, those who are systematically grandiose or self-abasing, and those who remain totally infantile in their ego development—all these particularly lend themselves to the study of ego ideal formation *in statu nascendi*. They also provide us with valuable leads in analyzing the milder character anomalies, for they are only a gross caricature of the latter. These unbridled, impulsive types constitute their own special category; so far, only Alexander[12] and Aichorn[13] have attempted to deal with them psychoanalytically in any detail. These patients are still uncharted terrain for psychoanalysis; because they generally do poorly in ambulatory treatment, they lack insight into their illness and, if put on the couch, never learn to use the fine tool of analysis. All these points we shall explore in detail. The available clinical material consists mostly of severe cases of character neurosis, which I selected for treatment in the Vienna Psychoanalytic Clinic. To avoid misunderstanding, I cannot forgo the condensed case presentations offered here, albeit they suffer the same short-comings as any other abbreviated case history in psychoanalysis. Their publication is especially warranted, since detailing our experience with such patients can afford the analyst the essence and specifics of the cases, minus the usual interpretations.

Our endeavor will take two concomitant pathways that will finally converge: the specific discussion of a type, hitherto poorly delineated in psychoanalysis, which we call, after Alexander, the "impulsive character," and, running parallel to this, an investigation into character formation in the light of this material. We shall in no way attempt a systematic presentation, something impossible with the induction-based empirical method of psychoanalysis. We must content ourselves with the demonstration of a typical developmental anomaly, occurring in the course of character formation and rooted in the better-known mechanisms of psychosexual development.

2. The Neurotic and Impulsive Characters: General Considerations

When approaching an uncharted realm in psychoanalysis, it is advisable to stick to phenomena of psychic illness that are already well understood. We may start with the assumption, clearly demonstrated by psychoanalysis, that no sharp distinctions exist between individual diagnostic types and their pathological manifestations or even between the "normal" and the "pathological." To begin with, the very concept of normality is unsatisfactory since the psychic state of normality, if there is such a thing, is a far greater problem, genetically and dynamically, than, for example, the well-known mechanism of hysterical symptom formation.

Nevertheless, if we try to differentiate the diagnostic types from the clinical pictures, or the sick from the healthy, we may rightly cite the fact that various controlling mechanisms arise from diverse combinations of psychic conflicts—conflicts pertaining to this or that clinical picture, as well as to the normal state. It is a convention, borrowed from the demands of our culture, that a certain set [of behavioral norms] constitutes the capacity for reality testing (and we cannot conceive of psychic health as anything else). It is a different story if we relate one form of illness to another. It is all the same if we say that the neurotic character, the impulsive character, and the psychopath constitute borderline cases between psychosis and health; or if we assert with Alexander that "every neurotic character carries within himself the seed of a specific form of neurosis"—which to a certain extent again bespeaks a borderline condition between neurosis and health. It depends upon our point of view in approaching the question and upon the profit we hope to derive from such a formulation. We lay no particular stress on the viewpoint we take here that the impulsive character is a borderline case between symptom neurosis and psychosis on the basis of his particular defense mechanisms. Alexander observes that "neurotic character types do not suffer from any gross appearance of illness, but their life-style is noticeably impulsive and often compulsive, as they are especially under the sway of unconscious tendencies," and that "a category of neurotic characters, certain impulse-laden criminal types, obviously suffer from a dearth of defense reactions." Alexander rightly points out the appearance of transitory symptoms in such patients whenever they fall subject to disappointment in analysis, and raises the question as to "whether the pressure of the etiologic factor—the damming up of the libido—is insufficient to find discharge through alternate channels, that is, in symptom formation, or whether the organism's defense reaction—repression—is inadequate to totally block the actual gratification."

To pose the problem in this way is not quite accurate. In the analysis of impulsive characters, one comes across amnesias totally comparable to the typical hysterical amnesia. Other repressive mechanisms, such as fragmenting experiences that are logically and genetically connected, displacement of guilt feelings, and reaction formation against destructive drives, are at least as intense in the impulsive character as they are in cases of compulsion neurosis. We shall illustrate this later with some examples.

We cannot talk about a weakness of individual repressions. Rather, our major focus will be on the following question: What are the determinants of the impulsive's lack of defenses? We shall have to examine the defect in the repression mechanism that enables the impulsive to act with a motility unavailable to the simple symptom neurotic. Even the case that Alexander published belongs to the category of character neurosis without a symptom. But, in addition to the impulsivity (which they mostly do not perceive as illness), the overwhelming majority of impulsives show all manner of symptoms, such as phobic and compulsive behavior, compulsive rituals and ruminations, and, particularly in female character neurotics, all the familiar forms of conversion symptoms may occur.

Grotesqueness is the hallmark of the impulsive character's symptoms. We may describe them as sick caricatures of the "stolid bourgeois" symptoms. A simple symptom-neurotic patient may think obsessively about killing his child or a friend —how banal and harmless this seems next to the impulsive's irresistible urge to roast his child slowly with a pine torch. We can no longer call it a compulsive drive (despite its similarity in structure) when one of my female patients derives her greatest pleasure from burning everything in her house and attacking her child with a flaming match. There are patients with self-castrating tendencies who suffer from a compulsive need to lose and misplace things—how mild they seem next to the impulse-driven female patient who can masturbate to orgasm only if she bleeds profusely from the vagina and who severely injures her cervix with a knife handle and winds up with a dropped uterus. Such patients are not lacking in common neurotic symptoms, but they have an extra something which simple neurotics lack. This "plus" not only separates them from the conversion hysterias, the anxiety neuroses, and the compulsion neuroses, but also brings a goodly number of them very close to schizophrenia. Such bizarre impulse behavior is not a rarity in the history of schizophrenics; later, I shall illustrate with case material how difficult it is, even after months of analytic treatment, to differentiate diagnostically between schizophrenia and transference neurosis.

All the cases I refer to are distinct from Alexander's in one essential point; a different yardstick will put them on a solid foundation. We always speak of the impulsive character whenever the predominant mode of behavior is dictated by the repetition compulsion and directed against the outside world. The diagnosis will also depend upon whether the behavior is expressed in undisguised, primitive drives, or whether it undergoes extensive secondary elaboration and transformation. Alexander's case stands out as one in which the patient was motivated by a deep need for punishment: he repeatedly (but unconsciously) chose friends who would cheat him out of his money until he wound up bankrupt in body and soul. He is one of those to whom Freud refers in *Beyond the Pleasure Principle:*

> The compulsion manifest here differs in no way from the repetition compulsion of the neurotic, even though these individuals show no sign of a neurotic conflict resolved through symptom formation. . . . Thus one knows people with whom every human relationship ends in the same way: benefactors whose protégés, however different they may otherwise have been, invariably after a time desert them in ill will, so that they are apparently condemned to drain to the dregs all the bitterness of ingratitude; men with whom every friendship ends in the friend's treachery; . . . lovers whose tender relationships with women each and all run through the same phases and come to the same end, and so on. We are less astonished at this "endless repetition of the same" if there is involved a question of active behavior on the part of the person concerned, and if we detect in his character an unalterable trait which must always manifest itself in the repetition of identical experiences. Far more striking are those cases where the person seems to be experiencing something passively, without exerting any influence of his own, and yet always meets with the same fate over and over again.[14]

Our cases show essentially the same "demonic trait"; however, the impulsive's behavior and experiences are permeated with undisguised, primitive drives, such as masochism, sadism, anality, orality, and the like.

It is possible that there are some cases of impulsive character who do not exemplify the question we raised vis-à-vis the defect in the repressing mechanism; they would show a different psychodynamic conflict.

We may now crystallize three questions that will occupy our attention:

1. Dynamically, what differences and what similarities does the impulsive character share with a case of simple transference neurosis?

2. Does the impulsive character possess specific defects in the mechanisms of repression? And, closely allied to this question—

3. If such defects exist, are they related to the defect in schizophrenia? If so, we would come closer to an understanding of general nosology; for psychopaths "mostly represent the first stage in the development of a full-blown psychosis" (Krae-pelin[15]), particularly schizophrenia; or, at least, they are close-ly allied to this category.

Our definition of impulsive character is certainly much nar-rower than the concept of "psychopath" generally held in the psychiatric literature. The latter is often too widely applied, so that symptoms found in otherwise stable personalities are dubbed "psychopathic." But even in the narrower sense, the definition of psychopathy is a hodgepodge because it fails to include the genetic aspects. Even Bleuler rightly deems every descriptive attempt at nosology a failure. Indeed, only by ex-amining the major mechanisms can we deal with the problem. As Bleuler notes:

> The clinical pictures in these cases show no clear-cut lines of demar-cation, either from one case to another, or from the norm.... I should say no boundary lines at all, for our yardsticks in designating a psychopath as sick are arbitrary. As a group, the totality of nervous disorders constitutes a broad spectrum of gradations and combina-tions, verging toward hysteria, in particular. Paranoid trends do not necessarily lead to paranoia in every case. One and the same patient may combine symptoms from a variety of clinical pictures ... in particular, disturbances of affect and neurotic manifestations are almost never absent....[16]

In determining what constitutes psychopathy, we see that the breakdown by types (which Bleuler himself uses), such as the vagrants, the impulse-laden, and the belligerent, the perverts, liars, and swindlers, and the antisocial and agitators, is quite useful for a preliminary orientation. The basic flaw in such attempts is that a single outstanding trait becomes the yardstick for classification in the group; what is overlooked is the fact, for example, that every impulsive (in Bleuler's sense) is as unstable as he is perverted; that every pervert is antisocial and also, therefore, a troublemaker. Bleuler's classification is borrowed from Kraepelin, though Bleuler has more clearly worked out the relationship of various forms of psychopathy to psychosis. Liepmann,[17] too, defined psychopaths as "pathological deviations from the norm, whose aberrations do not yet place them in the category of full-blown psychosis, since they lack severe symptoms."

The close affinity of psychopathy to psychosis (dementia praecox, in particular) caught the eye of those authors who did not stretch the concept of psychopathy to include emotional disorders like simple hysteria or compulsion neurosis. Similarly, for example, Kraepelin and Bleuler differentiate between neurasthenia and psychopathy, while Schneider[18] depicts the neurasthenic as an insecure, moody, and debilitated psychopath. Kraepelin designates one group of psychopaths as "arrested prepsychotics" and the other as "poorly nurtured types, whose upbringing was marred by adverse hereditary influences, congenital damage, or other early retardation. If the defects are mainly in the areas of affect and self-control, we consider them psychopaths." With regard to psychosis, Dickhoff[19] found that psychopathic bizarreness mainly leads to hebephrenia, paranoid schizophrenia, and paranoia. "Some psychoses, like simple paranoia, stem fully or largely from an exacerbation of psychopathic defects. . . . Where psychopathic defects are more severe, we find, on rare occasions, different types of psychotic disorders, of longer or shorter duration, offering no consistent pattern in their clinical picture or course. The prognosis for a single episode is generally good, but the probability of future breakdowns is high." Some authors, like Birnbaum,[20] Gaupp,[21] and Mezger[22], have a very broad concept of psychopathy. The last, for example, considers that "every deviation from the norm, every abnormality, is sickness, is pathology."

Thus far we have been using the terms "impulsive character," "neurotic character," and "character neurosis" indiscriminately. We must now set about cleaning up the terminology —surely not an easy task, considering the ambiguity of "character." To this end, we shall try to navigate safely between Scylla and Charybdis. On the one hand, we do not wish to err like the conventional scientist who far too often talks terminology and lets the living essence slip out of sight. On the other hand, we want to steer clear of the confusion that often arises when we use terms so broad in context as to leave the door open to all kinds of misunderstanding.

As a basis for our discussion, we shall loosely define "character" as the specific, personalized expression of one's psychic attitude toward the world; the specificity itself is determined by one's temperament and life experiences, in the sense of Freud's "ergänzungsreihe."

The neurotic character is seen, then, as one who shows more or less gross deviations from reality-oriented goals vis-à-vis sex, culture, and social adaptability. All types of neurotic characters have in common conflicting experiences and inner turmoil leading to insecurity in action and attitude. We know from psychoanalysis that these traits are the result of developmental disturbances, that whole fragments of personality are left behind and fixated at earlier developmental levels. On the basis of today's knowledge, the most flexible and cogent distinction between neurotic symptom and neurotic character would be the following: the neurotic symptom corresponds exactly to the personality fragments fixated at various levels, while the neurotic character is always the expression of the total attitude corresponding to this fixation. Therefore a fixation (and its resultant psychic conflict) always has two concurrent forms of expression: the neurotic symptom corresponding specifically to the fixation (hysterical vomiting, for example, as the expression of an oral-genital fixation), and the neurotic character reflecting the total personality disturbance caused by fixation of the fragment. Yet logically we must assume that even minimal fixations are not without effect on the rest of the personality. Thus every neurotic symptom is built upon a neurotic character. We may then speak of hysterical and compulsive characters (and possibly schizoid characters) upon whom symptoms sit like peaks on a mountain. The stage at which the developmental arrest takes place determines the neurotic character structure and its idiosyncrasies, as well as the neurotic symptom. The compulsion neurotic who seeks analysis because of an impulse to stab his friend in the back (compulsive symptom) shows a compulsive character as well: he is pedantically clean, loves order, and is overly conscientious. His character traits, like the symptom, contain features of the anal-sadistic stage. The expression "impulsive character" can mean, then, only a special form of neurotic character, a disturbance of the total personality marked by more or less unbridled behavior. We thus differentiate between neurotic symptom and neurotic character. By the same token, we must make a distinction between the act of a compulsive character (which is an irresistible piece of compulsive behavior) and the act of an impulsive character. The first is encapsulated, like a foreign body, in an otherwise stable personality and is ego-alien; the impulsivity of the second[23] is an attribute of the total personality and is mostly not perceived as illness, except in moments of clarity. The impulsive urges are mostly diffuse, not always aimed at specific objects or tied to specific situations, mostly fluctuating in kind and intensity, and largely dependent on environmental circumstances. These conditions stand in contrast to the rigidity of the neurotic compulsive act, which is largely independent of external circumstances. The interactions of the impulsive with his environment are generally more understandable and obvious than the encapsulated neurotic symptoms. The impulsive's urges never seem as senseless as the compulsive's, and he rationalizes his motives far more than the compulsive does.

The borderline between the impulsive and the schizophrenic (especially the paranoid and catatonic) is often just as obscure as the demarcation between the impulsive and the classical forms of transference neurosis. What separates the impulsive from the full-blown schizophrenic is a very lively, often outlandish manner of relating to the outside world. [I should like to cite] some cases from the Vienna Psychiatric Clinic[24] who were mainly diagnosed as "psychopathically inferior" vagrants, liars, or agitators. These showed such pronounced delusions of grandeur and persecution fantasies that the grotesqueness of their object relations was viewed as a reactive defense against autistic regression.

Furthermore, instead of the typical schizophrenic splitting of the personality, we find deep-seated states of depersonalization, which none of my pertinent cases failed to show. But we cannot consider depersonalization a valid criterion, for, as Nunberg[25] rightly stresses, the onset of most psychic illness reveals depersonalized states as an expression of libidinal withdrawal. Yet feelings of alienation, whether from one's own body or the outside world, are rarely as obvious or severe in transference neuroses as in impulsive disorders or schizophrenia. For several weeks, one of my cases (to be detailed later) had what looked like marked states of stupor during the interval between the Saturday and Monday sessions. She would lock herself in her room, cower on a sofa, and forgo eating or speaking. This condition always appeared when the analysis hit her hard or the transference seemed to waver.

Moreover, delusions of grandeur and persecution fantasies are absent, though ideas of reference[26] are not uncommon; the latter coincide with a propensity for feeling slighted and are characteristic of the simple transference neurosis. In an impulsive character, the feeling may snowball into a delusional belligerence. Reality-testing and awareness of ego boundaries remain intact, even if obscured by affect. Only three of my cases of impulsive character experienced auditory and visual hallucinations in the course of a long analysis. In one, they occurred in conjunction with a chronic hysterical condition; in another, during a sudden breakthrough of anxiety; and, in the third, they appeared in the course of an acute paranoid phase. Despite the frequent occurrence of hallucinations, especially auditory, in hysterical psychosis, it is noteworthy that the first case I cited, whose analysis I had to abandon because of a persistent twilight state, was mainly considered schizophrenic. Even the consultants on the case (Doctors Schilder and Jekel of the university teaching staff) did not venture to exclude the diagnosis of schizophrenia, despite the typical hysterical picture. In keeping with the latest psychiatric work on "the spectrum of schizoid types" (especially that of Kretschmer[27] and Bleuler[28]), we may make the following assumption: whenever schizoid hysteria regresses to hysterical dissociation, with production of a twilight state,[29] it activates latent schizophrenic mechanisms. We believe that schizophrenia (in the organic sense) cannot be qualitatively separated from hysteria and compulsion neurosis. Whoever shares this view must entertain the possibility that hysteria or compulsion neurosis can turn into schizophrenia under certain conditions which are for the moment obscure.

Consistent with the defect in repression, undisguised perversions are the rule in the case of the impulsive character. They are mainly from the sadomasochistic area. This special affinity to the realm of Freud's destructive drives we will come to recognize as a disturbance in superego development, as shown in his studies on the superego (ego ideal). Before discussing the specific developmental defects of the impulsive character, we shall briefly describe the typical character-neurotic disturbances common to all cases of symptom neurosis, in order to highlight the important differences. In general, our prime concern is a dynamic comparison of the impulsive character versus the impulse-inhibited character neurotic.

3. Ambivalence and Superego Formation in the Inhibited Character

Through Freud, we have learned to grasp how everything we call culture and civilization is based first on impulse repression and second on impulse sublimation. Every human being must recapitulate in abbreviated form, though in full detail, man's cultural progress from primitive savage to today's civilized man. Man is a pure impulse ego when put in this world —a world full of rules and restrictions to which he must conform. He thus renounces the major share of his demands for fuller gratification of a minor share later on. The adjustment comes about gradually in more or less clearly etched phases. This is not an automatic process like the growth of the body from the embryo. The "psychic embryo" needs very definite points of reference in its environment, which is a narrow one consisting mainly of the first nurturers. The latter become the objects of the first instinctual demands, as well as the gratifiers of these demands to a certain degree, particularly in the infantile period. They also play a decisive role in impulse frustration, which is the source of the earliest and most significant restrictions.

The impulsive character shows one essential feature: there is no final extinction of his drives, only buildup of drives, only change of goals and pathways. In short, he cannot make any drive gratification "pass away" without replacing it with something else. The existence of various stages of sexual development is dependent on such compensatory maneuvers. That is why a child's anal phase finds fullest expression only if the oral phase has been given up. Each renunciation brings about a splitting up of the corresponding libidinal energy flow. The most obvious results of the cleavage are as follows:

1. The drive is arrested in its original form, more or less

unchanged, while the partial drives are destined to play an important role in future sex life in the form of foreplay.

2. Depending on the nature of the impulse, a more or less energetic reaction formation takes place—for example, disgust as a defense against anal-erotic tendencies.

3. Sublimations can occur. Cleanliness, for example, is a primitive type of sublimation of anal-erotic tendencies. In later life, more complex types occur, which psychoanalysis reveals as key motivating forces in all fields of human endeavor.

4. Every erotic impulse serves to promote relationships with the nurturing figures. We can already observe the beginning of clear object love right at the oral stage; this culminates in the most intense object relationship in the genital stage, which we assume reaches its peak around the fourth year of life.

Within the mainstream of development, the splittings outlined above do not occur separately, but are closely interrelated. Thus object love plays an important role in reaction formation, for it makes the renunciation of the drive bearable. At this early age, the child is primarily a creature of pleasure (a pleasure ego, according to Freud), so it can and will only trade one pleasure for another. It adjusts to cleanliness mostly to please the mother. Stubbornness, particularly in the form of anal obstinacy, is an early-seen disturbance of this most primitive object love. When a child renounces a pleasure in order to please the mother, he makes demands on the mother to be his own. We see here the most primitive form of identification. It still contains a great deal of object love, for without it renunciation would not be bearable.

These early identifications are destined to pave the way for the later and final ones that have to do with present-day culture. But, before this, a stage of the most intense object relationships intervenes—Freud subsumed this under the concept of the Oedipus complex. The young boy more or less openly tries to take his father's place with the mother and wishes to eliminate him as an irksome competitor. The little girl adopts a similar attitude corresponding to her sex. A heterosexual object choice implies identification with one's own sex. But this simple oedipal relationship becomes complicated by a counterstruggle, which is outspoken in some cases and barely apparent in others:

the boy loves the father, also, and identifies with the mother, while the girl loves the mother and identifies with the father. Freud suggests postulating a "double Oedipus complex," since the bisexual tendency has a universal importance. This oedipal phase is among the most meaningful in human experience. Without exception, its conflicts stand at the core of every neurosis and mobilize powerful guilt feelings, the origins of which are still obscure, according to Freud. The guilt feelings develop with particular intensity into attitudes of hate, which are part and parcel of the Oedipus complex. I do not mean to imply that hate originates here; rather, it seems to be all primed and prepared, so that we come to regard the young child's first possessive and destructive impulses as early fore-runners of hate. We can show that no renunciation is accepted without producing hate, even in favorable cases where the hate is covered up by a substitute pleasure or substitute love object. It remains ready to break through whenever the renunci-ations are too intense.

Freud postulated an antithesis between libidinal and destruc-tive tendencies; the latter, originally directed against objects, yield to repression via reaction formation and sublimation. They constitute the basis for social conscience and ethical principles, and undergo special vicissitudes, as shown in studies on melancholy. That is, the destructive drives, turned against the self, underlie masochism in all its various manifestations. (We allude, in passing, to Freud's assumption[30] of a primary erogenous masochism which becomes sadism if directed to the outside, or secondary masochism if turned against the self.) As we see it now, the primitive impulse ego is held in check by a structure Freud dubbed "ego ideal" or "superego." It has its origin in the abandoned object cathexes and is made up of all those demands imposed upon the impulse ego by parents or other nurturers. In the final stage, the parents are given up as objects and retained in the form of the superego through the process of identification. Thus object relations become desexualized. The driving force [behind this process] is sadism in its sublimated form of moral "masochism" (as dis-tinguished from the erogenous form of masochism, the perver-sion): the incipient ego structure employs it to hold the impulse ego in check—in other words, to do the work of repression.

The Fulfillment of the Superego's Demands

Frustration stands at the very source of superego formation. It culminates basically in abandonment of the oedipal wish. Since we experience frustration at every stage of libidinal development, we may say that superego formation begins right after birth. Even training the infant to scheduled feedings is a frustration of the constant need to suck. Yes, we may go even further and tie the first nay-saying to birth, when the peace and pleasure of life in the womb come to an end.[31]

These primitive stages in superego formation now come to full fruition. Without fulfillment of the demand, "You must defecate at specified times and places," there would be no progress in libidinal development, for every impulse tends to repeat itself unchanged over and over again. But this fulfillment would be impossible if the other outlets for gratification, mentioned above, were not available. Later this changes. The more developed the child's personality becomes, the more he rebels against restrictions, especially in the narcissistic stages preceding the stage of full object love.

Almost all children, even those who remain healthy later on, go through a phase of intense rebellion against restrictions. In fact, extreme compliance may well presage a later well-known neurotic weakness—the inability to fight life's battles. The accomplishment of training is only partially successful then. The impulse ego more or less succeeds in maintaining itself against the superego's demands. Thus a part of one's development is arrested, and infantile gratification holds sway. Consequently the tension between unfulfilled superego and impulse ego gives rise to feelings of guilt. *The real ego, which is just unfolding, develops mainly from the gratified superego demands.* Fulfillment of ego ideal demands never stops; rather, there exists throughout life a constant oscillation between real ego and ego ideal. The ego ideal keeps growing; so do its demands, ever broader and more profuse. The more they are gratified, the more one attains what one aspires to be. Mainly, the typical conflict we see is between "being thus and so" (real ego) and "wishing to be thus and so" (superego). The inferiority complex (in Adler's sense) and its compensatory mechanisms are an expression of such a conflict. The real ego of the child differs from the adult's in one important respect.

The child's is composed only of fulfilled superego demands, while the adult's also contains sexual components—all those reality-based sexual strivings which do not conflict with the superego. Most neurotogenic conflicts are based on this evolution from a sex-negative to a sex-affirmative real ego, which normally starts some years after puberty. But the child's sex-negative real ego stems wholly from the prevailing moral upbringing. Psychoanalytically speaking, it would be highly feasible and desirable if even the child's real ego contained some sex-positive elements. There is much to be said for permitting the child some genital satisfaction: since childhood masturbation is part and parcel of physiological development, it is senseless, prophylactically speaking, to divorce the child's ego from such things. This would create a masturbation conflict, which is always felt in puberty and often becomes pathological.

Normally, the superego develops slowly. For the boy to remain healthy, this superego must be totally identified with the father; the same applies to the girl in relation to the mother. One must distinguish between positive and negative superego demands for the better monitoring of the drive-affirmative and drive-negative enjoinders corresponding to the two moralistic principles "thou shalt"[32] and "thou shalt not." The demands for impulse denial are fulfilled from the very beginning, the others much later. But emotional health requires that the superego contain impulse-affirmative tendencies. A totally naysaying superego creates a state of inhibition, such as one sees in the ambivalent, constricted, religious-ascetic compulsive. The [purely] drive-affirmative ego ideal creates a real ego that inevitably conflicts with reality. The impulsive character is such a type.

The Effect of the Partial Impulse on Superego Formation

How, then, does superego formation unfold in the healthy boy? In the case of a double Oedipus complex, we see heterosexual striving for the mother and identification with the father. Above all, identification with the father includes even the genital impulses, which, however, soon undergo repression and renunciation. The corresponding superego demand is, "You shall not desire your mother sexually or genitally." The fulfillment of this superego demand establishes the incest barrier.

Many positive superego demands are met as the boy tries to imitate his father and organizes his play around the central idea of being grown up—except genitally (Abraham). If this genital exclusion fails, if the inhibited genitality presses for discharge, symptom formation results. This sublimated ego ideal demand, stemming from identification with the father, runs as follows: "I want to be as big and strong and smart as my father." Pride in possessing a penis, if not inhibited by castration anxiety, leads to a disdain for the penis-lacking woman or little girl. But this prevents the occurrence of a mother identification, an identification that could be disastrous. As regularly shown in psychoanalysis, the incest wish reawakens in puberty, normally without entering consciousness, provided that the father identification is sufficiently strong and castration anxiety not overwhelming. Then, following a phase of genital masturbation with heterosexual fantasies, the incest fantasies cease and are channeled mainly into useful sublimations. To remain healthy, the young man must modify the ego ideal demand fulfilled in childhood, "You shall not desire your mother sexually," to read "You shall not desire your mother, but all other women are permitted." By excluding the mother, he overrides the sex-negative superego. Obviously, the guilt-free breakthrough of genital heterosexual tendencies is a must for later health. Identification with the father must be solid—indeed, it must even be able to override the father in the event of a strong, sex-negative father identification. But to triumph over the father, one has to have fully reached the phallic phase in childhood. Fully developed genital activity soon leads to sexual intercourse. The winning of an appropriate young woman leads to sexual devaluation of the mother. When the incest wish dawned on one of my patients, he condemned it with the following exclamation: "How stupid to desire one's ugly old mother, when there are so many young women around!" We may assume that attainment of normal genital object choices takes place through just such an alteration of incest ties. A favorable surmounting of the father largely frees the young man from the original father ideal.

Men with neurotic fixations show a rigid superego: characteristically, they must emulate the father image without regard to their own talents and abilities. Later we shall have more to say about the various forms of neurotic fixation stemming from the father-modeled superego ("I must be such-and-such, like my father"). Yet it is precisely the healthy men who show extensive deviations from the father ideal, in accordance with the formula, "You shall not be like your father." They are able to model themselves after qualitatively different father images and thus achieve a rich rounding out of their personalities. We cannot imagine cultural progress without an identification with qualitatively different father images—in other words, without the establishment of new ego ideals and dissolution of the old. This change of father ideal through a process of sublimation resembles a neurotic transformation of the type involving reactive superego formation (to be discussed later). The rebel who bucks society as a reaction against his father is far different from the one who models himself after a revolutionary father image, regardless of the father's beliefs. This favorable superego development can unfold only in the absence of binding libidinal ties to the father.

For the male, genital identification with the father assures emotional health, while his capacity to overcome the father ideal releases his creative powers. Similarly, for the female, vaginal identification with the child-bearing mother is a requisite for sound reality-testing and subjective well-being. As psychoanalysis has shown, the girl has to work harder than the boy at overcoming obstacles. At first, the wish for a penis veers her strongly toward a masculine identification. Therefore it is crucial for the mother identification to win out during the oedipal phase. This occurs most propitiously when the wish for a child supplants the wish for a penis. Psychoanalysis has shown that penis envy and penis wish come first and in favorable cases are replaced by the wish for a child.

Karen Horney[33] also pointed out another typical sequence, which I can verify from my own experience with female neurotics. In this second group, an intense wish for a child develops in accordance with the normal mother identification; it is, then, the denial of this wish which gives rise to the wish for a penis. In the first case, the child becomes a substitute for the penis, while here the opposite occurs: the fantasied penis becomes a substitute for the denied child. However, the first sequence seems to occur far more frequently.

For emotional health, which implies acceptance of the mother role, it is more propitious if identification with the mother occurs first and if the necessary willingness to give birth is prepared for long in advance. At first, the little girl is inculcated with the mother ideal. "You shall not desire your father sexually," and she represses her genital readiness. But generally, the infantile genitality of the little girl has a demonstrable clitoral quality, which is equivalent to the phallic eroticism of the boy. However, while the boy's phallic eroticism is fully compatible with his burgeoning, ultimate sexual role, clitoral sexuality conflicts with the woman's later, necessary vaginal attitude. In puberty, the change from clitoral to vaginal eroticism normally occurs following a reinforcement of the clitoral "thrust toward activity" as Helene Deutsch has emphasized in a recent lecture. The final renunciation of the penis goes hand in hand with a reinforcement of the mother ideal. However, we are still in the dark as to the sources of vaginal erogenicity. The theory of "the clitoral erotic shift" does not explain how the psychically determined clitoral eroticism, so phallic-aggressive in nature, undergoes transformation to the vaginal receptive state. According to Deutsch, what occurs here is a typical change from an actively directed impulse to a passively directed one. Be that as it may, from my own study of vaginally frigid analytic patients and certain aspects of vaginal eroticism, I would assume that the vagina is prepared to "take over" clitoral eroticism whenever it is strongly linked to the various types of erogenicity. Primarily, anal impulses appear to underlie vaginal eroticism. Vagina and anus are equally meaningful in the unconscious: "The vagina is leased from the anus" (according to Lou Andreas-Salome; see also Jekels[34] and Ferenczi[35]). In her lecture at the Salzburg Psychoanalytic Congress, Deutsch correctly derived the vaginal coital "sucking" movements from oral impulses. The vaginal eroticism of later life must stem from a preexisting forerunner in childhood. If, however, it is later synthesized from anal and oral qualities, the development of normal femininity must entail a partial return to earlier libidinal stages, following phallic renunciation.[36]

The normal postpubertal change of ego ideal, from purely drive-negative to drive-affirmative, applies to the female as well as the male. But the so-called double standard of sexual morality generally precludes this crucial change. The result is a striking and overwhelming majority of frigid women. Rough estimates place the figure at 80 to 90 percent, if we define frigidity as the incapacity for vaginal orgasm.

The popular concept of the "ideal woman" is mainly an offshoot of the "mother ideal," based upon oral and anal qualities. Hence the bourgeois ideal of the serene, tidy, frugal, submissive Hausfrau, who must cook, keep house, and hush the children. We could dispute the value of such a model; we could affirm that the male conjured it up for his own comfort and that he seeks in a woman the ultimate and all-caring nursing mother. But this has changed in past years, particularly since the war. The mother ideal has absorbed some elements from the father ideal: the woman should hold a job to help support the family; she should be active in all areas of human endeavor, like the man. This change (which not only women have wrought) in the time-honored ideal of pure motherhood serves to mitigate the conflicts surrounding renunciation of the penis. Whereas, before, the wish for a penis could only become the wish for a child, today there are many possibilities for sublimating the former. At first it may happen along father-image lines. But, by the next generation, perhaps we shall look upon woman's social and scientific activity as a consummation of the mother, rather than the father, ideal. In today's neurotic woman, the two ideals are mutually exclusive, since living up to the father ideal is a reactive maneuver, not a sublimation. Women who take "masculine" jobs are usually unable to give up the penis and fulfill the mother ideal (vaginal receptivity and child-bearing).

When we analyze women whose strong clitoral traits lead to reactive striving for the fatherly ego ideal, one of two things may happen. Either the woman gives up the penis and accepts in its place the child (and the man), or she partially sublimates the wish for a penis. For example, a patient of mine who had pursued studies in a frenzied, reactive way—perhaps rejecting all motherly attitudes and stressing masculine traits— achieved the insight that studying or other "masculine" pursuits could be quite compatible with femininity. She accepted her biological role of child-bearing and stopped clinging to the women's movement paradox that only as a man may one pursue studies or take advantage of "sexual freedom." Actually, the main goal of a women's movement should be to encourage the development of womanly qualities. Greta Meisel-Hess[37] quite rightly recognized the fallacy of its goal. The movement verged on breakdown for unconsciously wanting to achieve the impossible—that is, to give the woman the sorely missed penis. What analysis has accomplished in individual cases, social need has wrought for the broad masses of the working proletariat: it has made the motherly attitude compatible with social activity. In intellectual fields, education has made only some inroads. Here and there the dogma that social and scientific pursuits are masculine, that one must absolutely have a penis, has largely given way.

Let us summarize our conclusions so far:

1. To adjust to reality, the female must live up to the mother ideal, the male to the father ideal.

2. Both goals are largely dependent upon libidinal maturation.

    a. Fulfillment of the father ideal entails favorable activation of the phallic phase and overcoming of the castration complex. In so doing, the male can even free himself from the father ideal, if life's vicissitudes warrant it. The pregenital impulses are sublimated to striving in the social arena; the phallic remain intact.

    b. Fulfillment of the mother ideal entails renunciation of the penis and its replacement by the child (and acceptance of the male). Clitoral qualities mitigate against establishment of the mother ideal. The mother ideal draws far more upon the partially reactivated anal and oral impulses that help make up the feminine character. Clitoral eroticism is partly at the service of establishing vaginal eroticism; partly it is transformed into social activity and gives rise to an active character, for which the woman has a high potential.

3. Normally, in both sexes, the drive-affirmative demands of the ego ideal unfold in conjunction with the genital phase. For healthy female genitality, the only complication is that three organs (clitoris, anus, and mouth) must combine their erogenous qualities to create a reality-oriented libidinal position. At the genital stage, negative superego constructs exist only to keep the incest wish repressed. In a genitally satisfied individual, this negative superego scarcely makes itself felt, since the incest wish, normally destined for repression, has been discharged. All other negative ego ideals derive from the pregenital stages, inasmuch as the pregenital libido presses for discharge in unaltered form. The more one sublimates the

pregenital, the more the negative ego ideals harmonize with those of the genital phase, which are positive. This creates a well-balanced, goal-directed personality, fully attuned to reality. In all instances, the following polarities are reflected: health–illness, reality principle–pleasure principle; and, in the latter, genital–pregenital, positive superego–negative superego, sublimation–reaction formation.

Confusion of Psychosexual Identity

Let us now consider pathological superego formation in the light of faulty sexual identification. Here we will again emphasize the erogenous basis of dysfunctional ego development. A long-known and well-studied fact in psychoanalysis is the daughter's identification with the father ("masculine complex") and the son's identification with the mother ("passive-feminine attitude toward the father"). "In both sexes, the outcome of the Oedipus complex seems to devolve upon the relative strengths of the respective sexual predispositions" (Freud, *The Ego and the Id*). But the "sexual predispositions" make use of certain erogenous stages: for example, the passive-feminine attitude of the male is based on anal libido. But this is not the whole story. We know, for instance, that the male may identify with the mother and not give up the masculine attitude. This occurs typically in the narcissistic male homosexual. According to Sadger, this type quests as a male for the mother with a penis, yet prefers young men as love objects, to whom he can unconsciously play the guiding and nurturing mother. However, in almost all cases, there is an identification with the parent of the opposite sex.

The most crucial factors are the total bearing of the individual and the extent to which sexual confusion colors it—that is, how masculine the woman appears, how feminine the man. In other words, *it depends on whether the mistaken sexual identifications occurred in the ego ideal; or in the ego, thus reaching full realization.* Before going into details, let us indicate two possible causes of faulty sexual identification:

1. The faulty identification is present at the outset owing to a persistent[38] erogenous predisposition. Thus a strong anal predisposition will arrest a boy in the anal phase right at the outset and lay the basis for an intense mother identification.

A tenacious clitoral position will do likewise for the girl in regard to a father identification.

2. Another occurrence of major import enhances these erogenous attitudes. Analysis has shown that the superego evolves from that parental aspect which evoked the strongest ambivalence—in other words, from the source of the major frustrations. Owing to the inflexible nature of the libido, relationships of an object-libidinal nature do not lead to identification as long as they exist effectively. Only with denial and the resulting ambivalence is the libido withdrawn and the object incorporated into the ego. Normally, the girl has more or less obvious, positive feelings toward the father and ambivalence toward the mother—the boy, vice versa. If there are no further complications, this leads to a normal mother identification in the girl and father identification in the boy. Underlying these identifications is conflict, born of ambivalence. The boy experiences denial of the incest wish through the mere presence of the father, and the girl through the mother's presence. The analysis of neurotics with severely defective identifications shows a typical pattern: they have undergone the so-called normal frustrations not only from the parent of the same sex, but from the parent of the opposite sex as well, to a telling degree. As a result, they develop also an acute ambivalence toward the parent of the opposite sex. This leads to withdrawal of the object libido and introjection of the object and hence to faulty identification. A major determinant in ego development is whether the father or the mother is the chief frustrator of masturbation, child play, the incest wish, and so on. A further possible complication is the character of the frustrator, or the differences in character of the parents, which must find expression in the child's ego formation.[39] Should both these determinants of faulty identification occur, the final outcome can only be a "masculine complex" in the female and a "feminine complex" in the male. But the pervasiveness of the "Oedipus complex" and the "masculine" or "feminine" complexes is a cliché. The question today is no longer *do* they exist, but how they persist, how the conflicts are solved. Posing the problem this way will guard against one-sided explanations and open up fertile territory for psychoanalysis—the problem of the choice of neurosis. Even today, while we are still groping in the dark vis-à-vis the problem of specific etiology, here

and there we find definite types illustrating certain typical developmental defects. The attempt to evolve a psychoanalytic typology based on etiology would surely hinder every step of our research in this direction. Such a task lies at the end, not at the beginning, of our psychoanalytic work. Most of all we lack a psychoanalysis of schizophrenia. We must limit our efforts to formulating some typical mechanisms of character formation and leave the filling of gaps to broader, long-range research.

Mother identification in the male takes two typical forms corresponding to two different erogenous fixations: the mother identification of the ambivalent genital phase (Abraham) and the mother identification of the anal phase. Typical of the first is the narcissistic, more or less conscious homosexual described by Sadger[40] and Abraham.[41] These superficially self-assured "compensating narcissists"[42] show this characteristic libidinal development: they never overcome the Oedipus complex; they remain primarily fixated at the ambivalent genital stage,[43] but without any effective regression to earlier stages of development. The concept of the mother with the penis is of overriding importance here.

Two patients of mine dreamed quite openly about women —distinct mother images who had pipes or actual phalluses instead of female sex organs. In this fantasy, typically, two factors are working together. First, due to castration anxiety, the patient cannot tolerate the idea of a penis-lacking female genital—his unconscious clings to the notion that the woman has a penis (Freud); second, the female penis regularly has the meaning of the breast.

Such men never overcome even the oral fixation; active and passive fellatio play a large role in their sexual life. In the genital stage, they first take the road to a normal, genital identification with the father. When this fails (fear of castration by the father) they begin to identify with the mother. If they tend toward the active form of homosexuality and allow it expression, their love object is a young, effeminate male— again, the woman with the penis. However, on the other side of the picture, they play them against the mother, act as their protectors and initiate them into sexual life. With the opposite sex, they are fully or partially impotent. During the act of fellatio, passive and active sucking fantasies (mother identification) are, typically, both in operation. Two such patients of mine grew up fatherless. One was born out of wedlock and the other was bereaved of the father early in life. Absence of the father does not seem to hinder activation of the genital phase. On the contrary, it appears to intensify it, and, despite this, allows development of a mother identification. Whenever the boy fears castration from the mother, a mother identification is inevitable, especially if the mother is the main nurturer. Despite such an identification, these active, narcissistic homosexuals will even seek themselves in their love object, as Freud and Sadger noted. Narcissism underlies every love object. Precisely this search for one's self in the object ("narcissistic object choice," Freud) allows expression of the mother identification.

Mother identification on an anal basis is an entirely different story. Genital activity is absent; there is always impotence, mostly in the form of premature ejaculation, with or without erective potency. These patients have a soft, effeminate character and meekly submit to strong father images. Despite their fatherly superego, which is inordinately strong, they show an attitude of neurotic submissiveness. The father ideal is indeed present, often exaggerated, but never fulfilled; the wish to be a complete man, with social and sexual prowess, unfolds mostly in daydreams. Only the mother ideal is fulfilled, and this stands in sharp contrast to the unfulfilled father ideal. Such individuals show the mechanism of an inferiority complex (as emphasized by Adler) and typically tend to compensate in unrealistic ways. Because they cannot achieve the father ideal, they assume a martyr role. Behind this lurks the narcissistic belief that only they are noble and good, ultimately better than the rest of the world, at whose cruel and crass hands they must suffer (such is their reality-testing). In so doing, they flirt with cruelty, because they themselves yearn to be mean, crass, and, finally, as potent as their fathers.

Such a patient once expressed to me his belief that analysis could not free him of impotence—only his father's death would render him potent. He harshly condemned his father, who, like an animal, still tormented the mother with sexual intercourse at their ripe age of sixty years. The patient himself suffered from premature ejaculation of a urethral erotic type and also showed an anal fixation of a kind not often seen. Since early childhood, he had suffered from severe constipation. Especially while traveling, he often could not defecate for ten or twelve days at a time. The defecation had certain requirements: he had to squat over a pot filled with hot water or his mother had to give him an enema. Involved here was a crucial anal fixation on the mother. Even in earliest childhood, all he wanted was enemas from his equally anal mother. The whole family suffered from chronic constipation, but the patient's gave way in the course of analysis.

During his first attempt at intercourse, a remarkable thing happened: he turned his back on the woman and fell asleep. Analysis revealed that he had unconsciously expected an enema. He had displaced to this situation his specifically anal relationship to his mother. In his makeup, he was just like his mother: pedantic, clean, a lover of order, introverted, and depressed. And, like his mother, he feared and despised his father. Three older siblings had long since married and left home; he could not part from his mother. He felt obliged to be "the cement of this miserable marriage." The wish to receive an enema from the mother was, on a deeper level, the wish for anal intercourse with the father. The patient had never overcome the anal phase and had just barely activated an incipient phallic phase. Masturbation was anal and urethral. There were no genital fantasies of heterosexual intercourse, only the wish to lick the breast or vagina, to crawl between a woman's legs, to be tied up, and so on. In his fourth year of life, following a short period of genital masturbation, his older brother threatened him with castration. This totally suppressed his genitality. Then came the mother's reinforcement of the anal stage. He preferred platonic friendships with superior, virile men who were his exact opposite. He would admire them, feel inferior, and finally withdraw on some slight pretext. In analysis, he developed a strong passive-feminine transference and produced striking pregnancy fantasies during analysis of the constipation. In one of his dreams, he reported dropping turds which then disappeared, whereupon, "tiny little" children played in the room; but "tiny" and "little" also applied to the daily stools he produced. In other dreams, the analyst or a friend would impregnate him through the mouth (oral theory of conception).

After achieving the motherly ideal, with genitality excluded, he consciously added traits that were diametrically opposite to those of his father. The father was a busybody and opened every letter that came to the house; the patient was very discreet. The father was greedy and loved money; the patient despised it and squandered it. At home, the father was unrestrained in his personal hygiene: he would break wind regardless of whether other family members were around. The patient suffered severely from being unable to pass wind (a condition which disappeared promptly after the correlation was uncovered). The father was a woman chaser, the patient the opposite. Finally, by the patient's standards, the father was "oversexed"; he himself was impotent.

Thus the identification with the father was a reactive one. Not to be like the father, but the exact opposite, was the motto. Such reactive superego formations are often found in the character of neurotics. They figure in the makeup of the (inhibited) passive-feminine male; the same is true of the female with an inhibited masculine complex. They are most severe if the parents' character structures contrast sharply.

It is especially disastrous for the male child if a severe, loveless father aligns himself against the rest of the family. Mother and child join in a kind of tightly knit defense pact; the male child identifies with the mother, whom he loves and wants to protect from the father. In so doing, he renounces the genital position and retreats to the anal stage. He resigns in the battle against the father and never achieves adequate independence (neurotic resignation). Here the reaction toward the harsh father leads to a mother identification. A similar result obtains if the father is soft, gentle, and yielding, and the mother "wears the pants." Then we see not a mother identification, but an identification with the gentle father. There are feminine men who, in their object choice, always gravitate toward the harsh, strong mother; they love the "man-woman" to whom they surrender in a rather masochistic fashion. This requirement vis-à-vis the love object also colors the total personality.

The faulty identifications of the female are best studied in the light of the various types of frigidity. We can distinguish two main types of frigid women: those who have kept the motherly attitude and the wish for a child, and those who display a pronounced masculine attitude and often take on "male occupations." Such women either reject the sexual relationship *in toto* or marry but remain cold, harsh, and unapproachable. In the first case, we have a predominant, but inhibited, mother identification. The frigidity of such women is usually easier to remove than that of the second type, since it is rooted, ultimately, in an unconscious tie to the father, which was never given up. If the wish for a penis is present, they transform it into the wish for a child, in which case the child always symbolizes the phallus; however, the wish is never strong enough to form a masculine character. This calls for a finer distinction between the concepts "penis wish" and "masculinity wish." The latter is the broader term and includes the former, but the reverse is not always true. Despite their frigidity, women of the first type can develop an intense love for a husband or lover, but they run into trouble with fulfilling the motherly demand, "You shall not desire your father." If one frees them from the tie to the father and from the prohibition conveyed to them, the frigidity promptly yields.

Women of the second type have never recovered from their disappointed love for the father, so they incorporate him (according to the well-known formulation) and become what they could not have. Foremost are the wish for a penis and the compensated castration anxiety: they inhibit attainment of the motherly ideal and promote fulfillment of the fatherly model.[44] The early infantile history of such women almost always contains the fulfillment of a strong motherly ideal: the surrender as a woman (mother) to the father, and the wish to get a child from the father. Prognosis is more favorable in such cases because analysis can reactivate the repressed, reality-based position of the motherly ideal. In the course of analysis, one can transform the severe form of frigidity into the easier form (first type). But the analytic work is more difficult if the penis wish and castration anxiety appear before the development of the so-called normal, simple oedipal situation. For example, penis envy may arise from too-early play exposure to boys, or the love for the father may be scotched right at the start by the father's rejection. It would be fruitful to explore whether the acting-out masculine type of homosexual female had such a childhood and never activated an effective feminine attitude toward the father. I myself do not have any material in this area, but can recall cases which showed some deviation from this specific development. Roughly speaking, the libidinal development unfolds as follows: the father is harsh, rejecting, and lacking in love; the mother is kindly, depressed, and loving. Very early in life, the girl is severely conflicted with ambivalent feelings toward the father, which we know from experience weakens the capacity for heterosexual love and makes for a masculinity complex. All the child's love turns toward the mother. The tie to the mother is mainly oral and later gives rise to an intense, child-like submission to a mother figure; masculinity wishes may or may not be present. Such girls suffer from the demands of reality, and over and over again assume the role of a spoiled pet. The longing for the womb is also more prominent than in other cases and often leads to deepseated failure in reality-testing.

Tempted as we are to discuss further departures from reality-oriented character structure, we desist in view of the paucity of empirical findings. We are aware of the sketchiness of what we have presented so far, based on our analytic experience and current analytic theories. Yet concepts alone cannot do justice to the vastness and complexity of human experience. Those who can draw on their own analytic experience will be able to confirm our offerings, and indeed correct them and carry them further.

Faulty identification, that is, conflict-laden residues of the Oedipus complex or of other special experiences rooted in a specific, erogenous bent, can—with or without neurotic symptom formation—mold a person's character at the expense of his ability to test reality or enjoy life. The ego ideals are firmly built into the personality; the ego "identifies" with them. Indeed, we believe we have shown that the neurotic character is mainly composed of certain fulfilled ego ideal demands. The difference between the drive-inhibited neurotic character (which underlies every symptom neurosis) and the uninhibited impulsive character is to be sought in a specific disturbance of ego development. This we shall undertake to air in the forthcoming chapters.

4. Ambivalence and Ego Formation in the Impulsive Character

No matter how fruitfully psychoanalytic research delves into childhood experiences of the third to sixth years of life, we cannot deny that we lack the basic ingredients for fully grasping how the psyche unfolds. This is because in analyzing adults we can rarely go deeper than the third year of life. Earlier memories do appear from time to time, but they are so vague, so sparsely connected to the organic whole, that we dare not build any safe conclusions upon them. However, this we may safely assume for the present: what happens to a person in the first two years of life is more decisive than what happens later on. The child enters the highly critical oedipal phase with attitudes preformed, at least in broad outline, if not in their final detail. The Oedipus complex may be likened to a lens through which the rays of the impulses are refracted. They give this phase its special imprint and undergo far-reaching modifications through the experiences of this phase. Anna Freud's case of an hysterical symptom in a child of two and one-quarter years shows how obscure this realm still is.[45]

The difficulties in methodology seem insurmountable. So far, we have some reports of recent direct observations of children, but they deal only with children after the second year of life. We lack analytically trained child and infant nurses.

Another, indirect way to fathom the earliest phases of development is clinical research into certain forms of schizophrenia and melancholia, whose fixation points we believe lie in those early, postembryonal states. There are schizophrenics who show attitudes and mechanisms really corresponding to those of the infant or one-year-old child and, indeed, even to those of the embryonal state itself. Tausk's[46] case teaches us a great deal about effacement of the boundary between ego and outside world; Nunberg's[47] case is highly instructive vis-à-vis the most primitive sexual conflicts. Since certain forms of schizophrenia show partial or complete effacement of ego boundaries, along with definite infantile characteristics, it is not merely speculative for psychoanalysis to assume that the child's ego initially and gradually frees itself from chaos, that the ego boundary develops slowly, and that in this primordial phase of ego-unfolding the basis for ego maldevelopment is laid.

A pure impulse or pleasure ego confronts the stimuli of the surround, "identifies" with them insofar as they are pleasurable, and rejects them if they are unpleasurable, even if they stem from the impulse ego itself. The primordial pleasure ego has broader boundaries than the later real ego insofar as it deals with pleasure experiences (Freud),[48] and narrower boundaries insofar as it deals with unpleasure. Pleasure objects of the outside world are perceived as part of one's own ego; since the mother's breast is the central object of this first phase, we feel we may now comprehend the driving force behind the sending out of object libido from the narcissistic reservoir: the maternal breast must finally be recognized as belonging to the outside world; it must be shifted from the ego and drawn to the libidinal attitude attached to it. Thus, for the first time, narcissistic libido is transformed into object libido. The first objects are not total persons from the environment, but the organs of such persons insofar as they are pleasurable. During analysis, the object gradually dissociates into its component organs: for example, with regard to the mother, the breast especially stands out. Just as, in retrograde analysis, the tender libido leads back ultimately to a pure organ libido, so the infantile organ libido settles progressively into sublimated forms of tender libido. From the mother's breast, the libido extends to the dispenser of food, love, and relaxation, that is, to the mother.

The Effects of Upbringing

However, right in the very first phase of this important process, denial comes into play: the mother's breast is taken away. Gratification and denial oppose each other at every step of development; indeed, further development from stage to stage comes about only through denial. But in the juxtaposition of impulse gratification and denial we discern, with Graber,[49] the ontogenetic root of ambivalence. The child loves the gratifier of his impulses and hates the frustrator. Whenever hatred is older than love, as Stekel and Freud have pointed out, the reason for this is unpleasure at birth. This unpleasure is then forgotten, thanks to the effects of organ pleasure, and reappears in the form of birth anxiety or a wish to return to the womb, as Rank has observed, whenever the impulse denials turn out to be overly severe from the very beginning.

Thus ambivalence is natural and necessary to psychic development. Since everyone has experiences that engender ambivalence, we must ask ourselves: what is the added factor that makes ambivalence pathogenic? It depends on the following: the form and intensity of the denial; the stage of impulse gratification at which it was introduced; and the attitude of the child toward his nurturer at the moment in question. There are four main possibilities:

1. Partial impulse gratification plus partial, gradual denial, and through this, gradual repression. This situation represents the optimum developmental approach. In the state of partial impulse gratification, the child learns to love the nurturer and then accepts the denial "for the sake of" this person. We strive to achieve this optimum even in the analytic situation. The impulse satisfaction must be partial from the very beginning. For example, the infant must at the outset get used to feeding at certain hours. Denial must become increasingly strong without, however, leading to total impulse restraint. In this way, the impulse to be repressed can be sublimated or replaced by another partial impulse.

2. The impulse denial is not a gradual process, rather it proceeds full force, at every phase, right from the start. This is tantamount to total impulse inhibition, such as one sees in some cases of abulia. This is how in many cases—for example, through bottle feeding or total repression of genital masturbation—the capacity to love is inhibited. If the impulsive tendency is strong, the ambivalence conflict is biased in favor of hatred. This is true of many impulse-restrained compulsive neurotics.

3. Impulse denial is totally or virtually absent at the time of earliest development, owing to the fact that the child grows up without supervision. This can only result in uninhibited impulsivity. Since, sooner or later, the reactions of their expanding environment come into play, severe conflicts must of necessity arise. The first two possibilities we can verify analytically; the third we postulate in this extreme form. However, we are convinced that analytic investigation of criminals, prostitutes, and the like, will bring such facts to light.

4. As to the fourth possibility, we see, finally, the typical configuration of the impulsive character, according to my experience. In part it dovetails with the third possibility. In the analysis of impulsive characters, we find with surprising regularity that *an inordinate, unbridled impulse gratification was often met with a belated ruthless, traumatic frustration.*

Thus, for example, one such patient of mine was raped by her father, yet beaten senseless if she had anything to do with playmates on the street. Another patient grew up entirely unsupervised, indulged in genital games at age three (perhaps even earlier), yet was brutally beaten by her mother, who chanced to catch her at it. It commonly happens, for example, that children are strongly restricted in certain matters, but left entirely to themselves the rest of the time. Thus the father of a patient of mine insisted upon the children's eating everything but ignored their masturbating and playing with dirt. Often, too, children undergo minimal supervision and consequently develop poor impulse repression. Then, one day, the whole thing becomes too much for the parents, who now, suddenly—without warning and with great vehemence—sing a different tune. We shall spare ourselves the listing of further possibilities. Every insightful educator will have more to say on the subject. Inconsistent upbringing, that is, faulty impulse denial focused on a single detail, on the one hand, or sudden and belated inhibition, on the other—such is the common denominator in the genesis of the impulsive character.

Conflict, born of ambivalence, here takes on quite characteristic forms. Constant hate and fear for the nurturer may predominate, together with unrestrained impulsivity, occasionally reinforced by stubbornness. Or, equally often, an intense, unsatisfied longing for love is opposed by a hatred of the same intensity. Varying factors determine whether the result of such a development takes a sadistic or masochistic form. The incapacity for love is always gross here and much more outspoken than in simple symptom neurosis. Allied to this is a strong craving for love.

In contrast to the ambivalence of the compulsive, there is the distinct difference that reaction formation is lacking, and sadistic impulses are more or less fully lived out. In the typical compulsion neurosis, the ambivalence is displaced, in a seemingly senseless way, to details and to a lack of concern. Occasionally an impulsive will show such displacement, but typically the ambivalent relationship to the original objects or their corresponding substitutes remains persistently evident. In the impulsive character, the damage done by the nurturer's attitude is clearly manifest; in simple neurotics, such damage does occur occasionally, but, in most cases, this type of damage is not present or at least not more pronounced than in people who have remained healthy. The infantile experience of impulsive characters is riddled with severe traumas; symptom neurotics suffer none at all or, occasionally, only one. Typical experiences, such as healthy people undergo, like castration threats or primal scene, take on especially blatant forms in the impulsive character. This may be because the latter has suffered extreme cruelty for trivial offenses, experienced multiple seductions at the hands of the nurturers, or grown up in a sadistic environment. There are all gradations, ranging from the cultured person's unhappy marriage to the drunkard's brutal marital excesses. It is precisely this type of case that supports Freud's assumption that neurosis and pathological character formations are largely learned.[50] Clearly, an environment marked by scanty impulse control makes for poor ego ideal formation in the child; on the other hand, it allows the impulse frustration to be more brutal than necessary. Hence the typically acute and outspoken ambivalence of the impulsive, who can rightly say that he was not taught any differently. The unfeeling attitude of the nurturer is then reflected in the child's unfeeling attitude toward the environment. It would be quite incorrect to speak here of an absence of ego ideals. The impulse-negating ego ideal has been formed and is present, yet the impulse-affirmative superego has also been acquired at the same time. If this were not the case, unbridled impulsivity without neurotic constructs would result, as occurs in many psychopaths who lack such structures. The omnipresent feeling of guilt, especially in the masochistic forms of the impulsive character, points to a strong position of the ego ideal; the strength of the ego ideal position must be paralyzed momentarily if the impulsivity is to be effectively unleashed in defiance of it. This pathogenic superego formation appears in all impulsive characters; it is mainly conditioned by outside forces and countered by an inner force. At the same time, a constitutional factor figures here: an abnormally early sexual readiness, which can regularly be documented, that is, an overly strong emphasis on all erogenous zones. I would emphasize that the genitality of such patients reaches full development at an abnormally early age. In healthy individuals and mild neurotics, sexual activity in early childhood is the rule; the genital phase seems to peak regularly around the fourth or fifth year of life. Often the genital phase unfolds in a situation of fully repressed impulsivity: sexual and incest wishes never enter consciousness with full, sensual impact, but retain their full strength in the unconscious.

By contrast, impulsives have lived out their sexuality not only very early but also with fully conscious incest wishes. In this state of affairs, one libidinal phase does not free another, as in symptom neurotics; instead, the partial impulses stay more or less juxtaposed and of equal weight. These are the patients who have a characteristic history of polymorphous perverse child's play. Owing to lack of supervision, such patients see and grasp far more of adult sexual life than do the simple neurotics. The latency period is activated minimally or not at all. If we consider the importance of the latency period in human ego development vis-à-vis sublimations and reaction formation, we can gauge the damage done here. Puberty is ushered in with extreme breakthroughs of the sexual drive. Neither masturbation nor intercourse, which are taken up at a very early age, can afford relief, for the whole libidinal organization is torn apart by disappointment and guilt feelings.

The following case is very instructive in this regard. It illustrates such mechanisms as the sense of guilt, as well as the polymorphous perverse libidinal structure found in other types of impulsive characters. The latter I shall discuss in connection with a subsequent section on "isolation of the superego."

The Question of "Borderline Cases"

We are dealing here with a compulsion neurosis, but the diagnosis of schizophrenia is very much in the forefront.

A nineteen-year-old patient sought analysis because of a tormenting idea which always appeared whenever she thought she had done something bad: "The world is ending; it is totally annihilated." Whenever she was supposed to work, she thought compulsively, "Why should I do all this if the world is going to end tomorrow anyway?" The next day she would be utterly amazed that the world was not yet destroyed. Along with this there was no trace of manifest anxiety. Instead, feelings of great sadness and desolation accompanied the fantasy of world disaster: "Everything is dead, extinct; I often marvel that people are still moving around." These states of depersonalization were always connected with the world extinction fantasy, but they also appeared on other occasions several times a day.

At first she did not experience the end-of-the-world fantasy as an illness. In the beginning, she maintained very firmly that she believed in the possibility of world annihilation. Sometimes the patient would look lost, interrupt her speech, and stare absentmindedly; sometimes her speech was circumstantial. The first impression was that of dementia praecox. Her parents' observation that for days she was lost in dreams and unwilling to work bears this out.

One should mention that her older and prettier sister was well adjusted and showed no neurotic manifestations, as far as was known. The father was a functioning and capable individual, with a violent temper—irascible, domineering, intelligent. The mother was reportedly healthy, but a person with somewhat limited spiritual horizons.

The typically schizoid traits described above stood in sharp contrast to the patient's disposition, which bespoke an intense relationship to the outside world, especially toward the parents and sister, a relationship marked by stubbornness and spite. The patient felt extremely inferior and was unable to do anything, even though she was supposedly able to do everything. She would have liked to have learned every trade, understood mathematics, and grasped the construction of a machine, and she saw her inability as "an oppression of the woman by the man." Whenever she saw a girl learning to ride a bicycle on the street, she had the compulsive thought that a man must be more adept, and she viewed the learner's lack of skill as an oppression. Her inferiority feeling was closely tied to conscious, self-tormenting tendencies. For example, she learned how to cook and felt inferior; very often she did everything wrong consciously and deliberately, and her greatest delight was being scolded by her mother. She herself admitted that she did many things wrong in order to anger people and be reprimanded. She learned how to sew and purposely miscut material so that it had to be thrown out. In analysis, she was stubborn and inflexible, and after a few sessions asked why she didn't get thrown out. The world destruction fantasy always went hand in hand with the self-torment. But she even tormented others, especially her mother. She would purposely trip her to make her "fall and break her neck." She delighted in inventing cruel fantasies with both masochistic and sadistic goals. An example of the former: a sword is thrust up her vagina until it pierces the top of her head. Or she is made to walk barefoot and bleeding on a board spiked with nails.

The first fantasy related to her gonorrhea, which she pinpointed accurately as having occurred in her fourth year of life and which she presumably caught from a governess. She also dated the onset of her "craziness" from age four. For six years, she underwent special treatment, and the sword fantasy had a real basis in the pain she endured from dilatation of the cervix.

The second fantasy related to masturbation, which she had practiced continually since early childhood. It appeared at age four when her father yelled castration threats at her, tied her hands up all night, and inflicted other similar excesses.

Her sadistic fantasies can all be derived from the masochistic ones. Thus she told her mother: "Take a board, spike it with nails, and bash father's skull"; or, "Climb up on the window and throw yourself out. Meanwhile, if I happen to be eating, I shan't hinder you. I'll calmly finish eating and then go into the yard to have a look at your broken body." She perceived these outbursts as neither sick nor objectionable. She spoke them calmly without spontaneous feeling. On the other hand, she would throw herself on her mother's neck and kiss her.

It took long, hard effort in analysis to make the patient see that the world-destruction fantasy was related to her feelings of guilt, which actually stemmed from her sadistic impulses. The patient took special delight in "scratching" with bent fingers close to her mother's eyes, as if to blind her.

The patient felt oppressed by her father, but respected him because he was "smart" and the master of the house. The father, evidently a highly sadistic character, beat the children mercilessly (sometimes he even used switches) for the slightest infraction. Despite this—or, in keeping with her masochistic attitude, because of this—she respected him. Indeed, she even adopted his attitude and treated the mother just like the father did. She broke dishes in anger and was sarcastic and cruel to the mother; at the same time, she gave her rival, the prettier and preferred sister, all her love and admiration (later on, at least) just as the father did. The mother annoyed her "just by her mere presence." She thought her stupid, weak, overly permissive, and therefore unworthy of respect.

We can clearly see how the brutal fatherly ideal has taken over the patient's ego and how strong her father identification is. Next to this, at a deeper layer, lies the masochistic surrender to the father, which runs parallel to the sadistic attitude toward the mother. Yet both sadistic and masochistic tendencies are fully conscious. Thus we see here the typical aspect of this case—precisely in the fact that such tendencies are fully conscious and not buried under the strongest repression in the manner of a simple compulsion neurotic. Our patient also failed to show the typical overscrupulousness of the latter category; on the contrary, she was without qualms most of the time.

An analogy to the compulsive's overscrupulousness is expressed by the central symptom, the world destruction fantasy, which corresponded to tremendous guilt feelings toward the mother (and later to broader and deeper determinants), but was associated with simple, trivial occurrences. But it was just this displacement of guilt feelings to trivial matters that made the manifest sadistic attitude possible. During analysis, this connection was correctly reestablished; but now the patient began to feel her sadistic attitude toward the mother as a compulsion. At this point, the compulsive character of the impulsive was transformed into a typical compulsive symptom.

The typical case of compulsion neurosis presents with an undisguised compulsive thought or impulse, and the guilt feeling is directly related to the symptom. In the sharp separation between sadistic impulse and guilt feeling, we see one of the typical mechanisms of the impulsive character. As further evidence, we may note the following: in the hyperscrupulous compulsive who has completely repressed his sadistic impulses, guilt feelings are connected to trivial events, just as they are in the impulsive.

Later on, we shall have to deal more exactly with the key question concerning the impulsive character: what makes the separation of guilt feelings from manifest sadism possible?

I should like to present briefly the libidinal aspects of our case, in whom sexuality is unrepressed to an extreme degree.

The patient masturbated almost every day without orgastic sensation and with abundant masochistic fantasies. There was no intercourse. In this respect, we can label her libidinal structure as totally polymorphous perverse. One masturbatory fantasy was that she and her father would eat stuffed vaginas that had been excised and filled with dirt. We have, therefore, components from all three libidinal levels: eating (oral), vaginas (genital), dirt-filled (anal); and the whole thing is experienced masochistically (she is forced to do it). Manifest coital fantasies of a normal nature played a minimal role. The oral component of this fantasy has its special history. During childhood, she and her sister suffered from difficulties in eating. To combat this, the family doctor (!) recommended that they be forced to eat by any means available; should they regurgitate, they should be forced to eat the vomitus also. This happened repeatedly. It is readily understandable that repression and sublimation of oral and anal tendencies failed, so that the patient was still eating dirt and vaginal secretions in her seventh and eighth years of life. At the time of the analysis, the patient still took great pleasure in smearing vaginal secretions between her fingers.

Fantasies of the womb also loomed large in this patient's symptomatology, along with the libidinal development. A vivid visual image went hand in hand with the world-destruction fantasy, which in the final analysis was a temporary regression to the womb, dictated by feelings of guilt. The patient saw herself lying in a "globe." The drawing is by the patient herself: (a) represents the globe; (b) are the eyelids, which "like shelves line the interior and run to the body"; (c) represents herself. We do not hesitate to take this for a womb situation.[51]

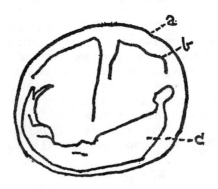

We may better understand the libidinal structure of such patients if we compare it to that of a classical case of hysteria and of compulsion neurosis, respectively. In the analysis of a pure anxiety hysteria, we find a repressed genital libido as the central pathogenic factor. Moreover, even if a different libidinal component emerges as a symptom or in the course of a depth analysis, we still have no reason to doubt that the main fixation in pure anxiety hysteria is at the genital stage. Hysteria, according to Freud, is an illness of the genital phase. This is true even in a conversion hysteria of an oral type—a case of hysterical vomiting, for example—where we find a central oral fixation in the libidinal pattern. Analyzing the total personality of the hysterical character, and the meaning and cause of the oral symptom, soon tells us that the oral zone has acquired a genital meaning ("displacement upward"), as Freud and Ferenczi have pointed out. In a classic compulsive, whether he shows sadistic impulses or cleaning rituals based on anal eroticism, the pregenital anal-sadistic fixation always occupies the central position (Freud); it gives rise to the symptoms, and it gives the compulsive character his specific stamp (overconscientiousness, orderliness, and so on, as reaction formations against repressed sadism and anality). In melancholia, the oral fixation is central, as Abraham conclusively demonstrated—a fact which every analytically trained clinician can easily prove for himself. In the mixed forms of compulsion neurosis and hysteria, a depth analysis can, without difficulty, reduce the various symptoms and character traits to their corresponding fixation points. True, there is still a myriad of unsolved, crucial problems centering around the developmental thrust from the anal sadistic to the genital stage—which really has to do with the problem of specific etiology. Nevertheless, in the milder and purer forms of hysteria and compulsion neurosis, we do delineate circumscribed fixations and developmental blocks of a portion of the personality with more or less sharply defined libidinal positions. In the extreme impulsive character, like the case described, we can never make such an evaluation. If we try to relate a host of attitudes and symptoms to a genital or anal fixation, we must ascribe as important a role to the oral fixation. Even with extensive analysis, we cannot find a common fixation point at a given stage of libidinal development, but, rather, a more or less equal juxtaposition of all known partial impulses in combinations and permutations which most of the time cannot be sorted out. We get the impression—to use a drastic metaphor—of a bull unleashed in the china shop of infantile development.

Our case shows a lasting, marked ambivalence toward the father and mother, which is especially expressed in the cruel words and deeds toward the mother. The patient's superego is totally oriented toward the male. She admires her strong, rough father and acts just like the father toward the "dumb" weak mother. The identification is fully conscious. Inferiority feelings, so prominent in her complaints, hark back totally to the father identification and to envy toward the sister who is her father's favorite.

Analysis revealed the following about the father. He had almost certainly inflicted severe damage with his sadistic attitude; he had provided the model for the sadistic ego ideal; but, most of all, he was very likely a party to [his daughter's] defective impulse repression. He had approached the children with unveiled sexual intent; indeed, I strongly suspected that he had given the patient gonorrhea when I learned that he himself had suffered from chronic gonorrhea. The patient herself dated the onset of her illness to around the fourth year of life, the exact time of the gonorrhea infection, and she always felt immensely shy toward the father. She was always fantasizing being "raped" by him.

The father is also implicated in the poor control of anal impulses. He forced the children to eat vomitus, thus fostering coprophilic tendencies, which at any rate were present to begin with.[52] It is understandable that anal repression was defective. He beat the children mercilessly for the slightest transgression but felt completely free himself in anal matters. One might object that the older sister remained healthy despite growing up in the same environment. To this we counter the fact that she was always held up as a model to the younger sister and was favored and overesteemed in every way, a factor which was surely enough to turn the scales. Moreover, we know nothing about the sister's libidinal vicissitudes or what had really promoted the favorable outcome. She hated the parents as much as the patient did but had opportunely freed herself from home.

The case shows pronounced schizophrenic mechanisms side

by side with classical compulsive mechanisms. Many readers will make a diagnosis of schizophrenia. The major compulsive symptom, the rumination about the end of the world, is schizophrenic both in content and in the way it is perceived. The patient tends toward autism. The absence of repression, the conscious awareness of the sexual wishes, bespeak schizophrenia; yet, all the grosser dissociations of affect and confusion are lacking for a strict diagnosis, nor are there hallucinations or delusions. Although we do not expect to make a diagnosis, it is still not unproductive to ask whether we are dealing here with a schizophrenia or a compulsion neurosis. Only future developments will tell. Were we to apply Bleuler's[53] broader concept of schizophrenia here, we would tend toward a diagnosis of latent schizophrenia with compulsive symptoms. At the same time, we must rule out dementia praecox, according to Kraepelin's narrower definition,[54] but we may consider the patient a kind of "psychopath" which, as Kraepelin notes, is an early precursor of true psychosis. In the final analysis, we see that the whole question becomes a struggle over terminology.

The question of borderline cases warrants considerable discussion, since most patients with this clinical picture show not only various schizophrenic symptoms but also an oscillation of their libidinal structure back and forth between autism and object cathexis. In almost all severe cases of impulsive character, we must raise the question as to whether a schizophrenic process exists.

From the psychoanalytic standpoint, we can approach this question only in the dynamic context of a libidinal position. Even in psychoanalysis we speak of "latent schizophrenia," but this does not imply the actual existence of a schizophrenic position that is merely covered over by transference-neurotic symptoms and attitudes. Such an assumption would diametrically oppose the libidinal-dynamic principles we have come to understand. It would impart a static quality to an area we see as purely dynamic. In the absence of typical schizophrenic symptoms like stupor, delusions, word salad, or hallucinations, we cannot say there is a schizophrenia present, nor can we talk about latent schizophrenia. But, in keeping with the above, we must always remember that what we are talking about is a greater tendency toward the schizophrenic withdrawal of libido from the outside world. There is often a deterioration from an overly strong narcissistic position to a "latent" schizophrenia. On the other hand, there are neurotics who could never be called schizophrenic, yet who show a narcissistic position matching in intensity that of the schizophrenic.

To what degree does a schizophrenic's narcissistic position differ from that of a "narcissistic," inaccessible transference-neurotic's? This is still a question without a satisfactory solution. And it is not our purpose to deal with it here. However, analytic research of "borderline" cases like our patient warns against the assumption of a "ready-made" schizophrenia, as it were, which subsequently "becomes manifest."

I treated a forty-year-old female psychopath who, from earliest childhood and particularly since puberty, presented the clinical picture of "latent" schizophrenia. She was a complaining patient, who thought she was pursued by fate and maltreated by everybody. She also suffered from states that differed little from catatonic stupors, in addition to phobias, compulsive rumination and impulses, and conversion symptoms. At the psychiatric observation ward, where she had been a number of times, she was diagnosed once as a psychopath, another time as a compulsive, and finally as a paraphrenic, without any appreciable change in the clinical picture since puberty. There are some typical compulsives who, owing to their cyclic depressions, belong in the group of cyclothymic disorders and seem to be totally excluded from a schizophrenic diagnosis. Again, there are others who show a special relationship to schizophrenia (our patient, for example). The whole problem becomes clearer if we free ourselves from the prejudice (still held even in analytic circles) that schizophrenia, owing to its organic nature, is a basically different illness from the rest of the "psychogenic" neuroses. (Jaspers[55] speaks of a "schizophrenic process.") Even Schilder[56] still holds to this. In psychiatric literature, we often do not see the connection between the outbreak of a psychosis and the actual history, because we are trapped by the prejudice of a ready-made, organically preformed psychosis. Hartmann[57] had occasion to observe two sisters who became schizophrenic at the same time, coinciding with their father's death. How can this be compatible with the idea of a preformed psychosis?

There are two theories in particular concerning this question.

One postulates that schizophrenia is caused by internal secretions; the other assumes that schizophrenia is constitutional, especially since Kretschmer's work.[58] Of course, Freud has always thought about an internal secretory process even in the etiology of transference neurosis, and his whole theory of "erogenous zones," so central to his theory of the neuroses, is based upon this assumption ("sexual substances"). However, according to this schema, transference neurosis would not differ basically from schizophrenia. Even the assumption of a specific constitution, Kretschmer's "schizoid group," for example, does not contradict a psychogenetic viewpoint. The schizoid group covers a much broader territory than the realm of schizophrenia. Compulsives, and, in particular, hysterics, also belong here. Likewise, the finding of pathological changes in the cerebral cortices of old, burned-out schizophrenics does not contradict our view. In the first place, we do not know what kind of changes (cytoarchitectural, perhaps) may occur even in hysterics and compulsives. Thus far, no such changes have been found. Moreover, the rarity of pathological changes is markedly disproportionate to the high incidence of schizophrenia—even if we do not consider whether such changes in burned-out dementias represent atrophy from lack of activity. If this is so, the transformation of a compulsion neurosis into a schizophrenic disorder remains a problem, and it might be of utmost help not to erect a wall between these illnesses. The relationship between them is all too obvious.[59]

During the analysis of an impulsive character, we can observe transitory delusions *in statu nascendi*; moreover, we see how an irresistible impulse, normally not felt as a compulsion, is transformed into a compulsive act. At this point, the content remains and only the form is changed. During analysis, in conjunction with a homosexual transference which became acute, one of my erythrophobes developed a fully systematized delusion of persecution of five days' duration. He was presumably an Aryan, I was a Jew and therefore wanted to hurt him; he felt I was watching him and he was afraid of me. I was a sensuous pig, I had sensuous lips, and I looked at him sensuously. All he had done was to project onto me his homosexual wishes, which had just come up in analysis. When this phase passed, he realized the connection of the wishes to himself and he would reproach himself for being lascivious and having intercourse with his eyes, etc. As Helene Deutsch[60] has stressed, excessive neurotic distrust, especially in compulsives, stems from the fact that their own repressed sadistic tendencies are projected onto others. We know the role played by distrust in cases of paranoia.

A patient whom we shall discuss later—in whose case schizophrenia could not be totally ruled out—developed acute transient auditory and visual hallucinations during analysis. She had learned of the death of a loved one and wished to deny it. During a session she heard this person cry out and pound on the door, and saw her standing clearly in front of her. A strong denial of the experienced loss—the wish that the deceased would live—was fulfilled through hallucinations.

In all such cases, a transient clouding of reality-testing occurs, which enables the patient to experience delusionally the content of his or her experience. Cases of the type we are discussing are especially prone to a transient clouding of reality-testing. This undoubtedly has to do with an acute withdrawal of cathexis, with narcissistic regression. When the ego is flooded by narcissistic libido, this must have a distinct effect upon that part of consciousness which receives perceptual stimuli and controls reality-testing (Freud's "perceptual system").

It appears that the road connecting the "narcissistic reservoir" to the object-libidinal position is far broader in such cases than in the simple transference neurotic. The roughest assumption we can make is that the "breadth" of communication between ego and outside world implements this great tendency toward regression. The libido of such patients is in a perpetual state of oscillation. At the slightest denial or disappointment on the part of reality, an acute withdrawal of cathexis ensues. Freud has already clarified the difference between this and the libidinal regression of simple transference neurotics who have no schizophrenic mechanisms: after a disappointment, the neurotic withdraws libido from real objects and recathects fantasied objects with it. The schizophrenic, or the neurotic with schizophrenic mechanisms like our main case, deflects the withdrawn libido into the ego and even renounces cathexis of the fantasy. This is how the cathecting of a fantasy with object libido serves as a protection against narcissistic regression. A broader regressive pathway to autism, no matter what its nature and origin, will unfavorably balance the outcome against the cathexis of the fantasy.

5. The Isolation of the Superego

The case we discussed in the last chapter may serve as a model for the group of impulsive character types showing partly neurotic (that is, compulsive) and partly schizophrenic mechanisms, such as we had occasion to observe so often at the psychiatric clinic. Analytic exploration of such a patient gives the observer trained in analysis a deeper grasp of cases with similar mechanisms. Yet even this case left many questions unanswered—mainly because, on the basis of the ego ideal structure, we could not extract a precise explanation as to why the repressing mechanisms were defective. For the hallmark of the ego ideal—the striving to be like the father in every way (fatherly superego)—applies even to the female compulsive since the repressing mechanisms are intact except in the realm of the symptoms. We are well aware that in seeking solutions to key questions we must wait for the right case which then, with a single stroke, clears up the gray areas in many a similar case.

A patient with genital masochism, whose character structure remained completely infantile, now furnished me with the long-sought clarification. Her analysis began about a year and a half ago. Her ego structure was relatively transparent, much simpler than that of the last patient, for example, or of the impulsive characters I had been treating concurrently or previously. The basic libidinal positions had remained quite constant since earliest childhood, so we did not have to work through the usual confusing complications that are superimposed later.

Let us recall, once again, our initial problem and briefly restate it: how can unrestrained impulsivity coexist with repressions and amnesias? In other words, what does the ego ideal —which is undoubtedly present and which mediates the well-known function of impulse repression, but in a defective manner—look like?

A twenty-six-year-old single female came to the psychoanalytic clinic because of continuous sexual excitation. She longed for satisfaction but could feel nothing during intercourse, not even entry of the penis. She would lie there "tense" and "listening for the satisfaction to come." The slightest bodily movement would dispel every upcoming pleasure sensation. She also suffered from insomnia, anxiety states, and compulsive masturbation. She would masturbate with a knife handle up to ten times a day, reach a high pitch of excitement, then stop the friction to avoid consummation. She would do this to exhaustion until, finally, she would have no climax at all or she would deliberately make her vagina bleed and derive satisfaction from the accompanying masochistic fantasies. The vaginal bleeding was a condition of the satisfaction. She fantasied that she penetrated deep into the uterus: "I can only be satisfied in the uterus." During masturbation, she fantasied that her vagina, which she called "Lotte," was a little girl. She would carry on a continuous dialogue with it while playing both roles: "Now, my dear, you will be satisfied—look [during analysis] the doctor is with you. He has a beautiful long penis, but it has to hurt you." Lotte: "No, I don't want it to hurt me!" (She would cry.) "You have to suffer, this is the punishment for your lewdness, you are a slut. It must hurt even more—the knife must come out through your back." And so on in the same vein. Masturbation represented a grievous sin for which no punishment was too great. She had constant fantasies about all the men she knew, and even about "Mami," a female analyst who had treated her three years before for a period of eight months. (After a two-year remission, the patient relapsed.) The patient's father, older sister, and younger brother were apparently healthy and functioning. The father was unhappy in his marriage and henpecked by a domineering wife. The mother was bossy and strict, but extremely efficient. She always ruled the roost. An older brother was serving a jail sentence for "rape" at the time of the analysis.

The patient felt mistreated and rejected by her mother. Even in the transference, which was very strong, she played the role of the rejected, unloved child (to such a degree that it almost brought the analysis to a standstill). Once the attachment to the first therapist was dissolved, the ambivalent feelings for the mother came into full awareness. She longed for "Mami" but could not recognize in this [the disguised longing for] her own mother, because she was unable to love a mother who perpetually rejected, beat, abused, and neglected her (this corresponded to reality). She had fantasies of nursing on currently chosen "Mamis," and the longing for the womb was uppermost. Her protestation about having to suffer for others and being punished for their wrongdoing was cleared up when we uncovered the following fantasy she had had as a child of eight. The mother was situated in one boarding house, the patient in another. The mother, who was unhappily married to the father, often entertained a tall gentleman whom she called "the count." The patient was once introduced to this gentleman. Thereafter she believed that the mother rejected her because she was the count's child, an upsetting situation for the mother. She had fantasies of being raped by the count with the mother's help. (It was not clear whether this was fantasy or reality—consider her masturbatory fantasies!) She would feel a big penis enter her vagina, and this would cause her great pain. The room was dark and someone was standing nearby shouting to her to be still and not cry out.

Analysis later uncovered a similiar fantasy (or dark memory?) from her fourth year of life. Two men, tenants of her parents, carry her into their rented room. One is holding her and the other forces his oversized penis into her vagina. She wants to scream but cannot. She also had full memory of sex play with boys her age in a basement. At age ten, she had coitus with an older brother. At age six, while playing with her two-year-old brother, she saw his penis and tried to insert a knitting needle into it. The penis bled, and the patient pulled it. The boy cried, and the mother beat the girl and pulled her hair. At age twelve, she got a job as a babysitter. Every night for two years, her employer stimulated her but did not consummate. At age fifteen, she believed herself pregnant; menses ceased for two years and returned after she broke off her first analysis. At this time, she conceived the idea of tying a piece of wood to her vagina. Subsequently, she often came to analysis with a knife in her vagina; obviously this was possible only through vaginal spasm. She was unable to fall asleep without having a knife stuck in her vagina.

The onset of her current masturbatory practices dated back to the age of fifteen, after she spent a night with her father in the same room. She had had a nightmare which she could not remember and awoke early lying on the floor. The bed was broken. Her father asked her what she had done during the night but offered no further clarification. To date, analysis has not been able to solve this detail. Yet everything pointed to the fact that the father's nearness had excited her and led to the nightmare. It is most likely that the patient had then tried to masturbate.

She suffered a relapse after making the acquaintance of a sadist who beat her with whips, pulled her hair, cursed her, and forced her to criminal activities as well. Twice she was forced to steal for him and bring him little girls. On top of this, she would call him her best friend, say she could not live without him, and for hours would run after him through the streets of the town. In analysis, it was possible only with great effort, under threat of terminating treatment, to separate her from him. She immediately transferred the masochistic attitude to the therapist, brought a whip to the analytic hour, and started to undress to be beaten. Only the strictest intervention could keep her from doing so. She would run after me in the streets and look for me at my home at ten o'clock at night. She could not bear it any longer; I would have to have intercourse with her or beat her up; she had to have a child of mine because only I could satisfy her. So it went for about eight months; no exhortation made any impression upon her. Whenever she did anything wrong, she would masturbate with more vigor and frequency: "For punishment, I must be slaughtered." In the eighth month of analysis, she attempted to poison her older sister and her husband. (Owing to certain circumstances, which we cannot divulge, we know this to be a fact.) The patient had amnesia about the entire matter but revealed the attempt through her dreams and through her especially punitive masturbation. Some days earlier, she had brought rat poison to the analysis: she "loved it so much" that she had to collect it.

Only with the strictest prohibitions, under threat of termination, could the patient be maintained in analysis.

In the fourteenth month of analysis, during a calmer phase, scenes from the parental bedroom were recalled from total amnesia. Things she had witnessed, sadistic notions about the sexual act and birth were cleared up here, and a part of her anxiety was dissolved. The patient got a job and remained fairly well.

Characteristically, she now developed an eating compulsion and gained a great deal of weight. This corresponded to fantasies of oral impregnation. Her tendency to prolong the analysis ad infinitum had to be countered with a deadline for termination (an additional six months) since the major portion was broken through. Masturbation with guilt feelings flared up following a discussion of bedroom scenes and had to be interdicted. This prohibition was especially advisable in view of the obvious local damage, such as uterine prolapse and flexion.

The appearance of the undisguised incest wish, hitherto repressed, brought no self-recrimination. On the contrary, the patient now had conscious fantasies of having intercourse with her father and bearing him a child. At times, her fantasies mounted to vivid hallucinations. She sees a devil who mocks her, since she will be unable to resist masturbation after all; her efforts are in vain. Sometimes he has the features of the count; at other times, he looks like the mother. The devil represented her sadistic and incestuous wishes, against which she had to defend herself; it also represented her mother; and, most of all, her father in the context of the forbidden object.

Let us tie together the threads of the case. We are dealing with a patient who remained infantile not only in her sexual makeup but also (and especially) in her ego development. The masochistic genital masturbation is impulsive and uncontrollable. Originally it is not experienced as a compulsion or regarded as pathological. The verbot of the introjected mother, "You shall not desire your father, nor practice masturbation," is transformed into, "You (the genital—the patient) are a lewd whore, and you must die by masturbation for your sins." The masturbation therefore represents a compromise between the gratification of the incest fantasy ("I can only be satisfied by a large penis in my uterus") and a disastrous coupling of death wishes and destructive tendencies with genital pleasure. In the act of masturbation, she identifies her genital ("the little girl") with herself, and her ego with the punitive mother. *The overly severe superego is borrowed entirely from the mother and its demand is fully gratified during the act of masturbation.* This borrowed part of her ego, the introjected mother, is opposed by her own undeveloped ego, which shows the following features:

1. Masochistic surrender to the punitive mother (later to the superego).

2. Complete identification of the genital (the little girl) with the pleasure ego.

3. A fully repressed genital object relationship to the father.

4. An oral and womb relationship to the mother.

The penis wish, though present, did not lead to formation of a male character structure. The patient remained childlike and feminine. This included even the highly charged, conscious wish for a child.

In the sexual area, we may assume there is a major fixation *at the genital stage.* It is masochistically fixed by an intense castration complex and stands in competition with the oral fixation to the mother. However, we must wonder whether in this case a fixation of the ego exists. In considering this, let us proceed to ego development in simple symptom neurosis.

Taking the compulsive for comparison, we easily recognize that the ego development here is far in advance of the sexual development. In the sexual realm, the pregenital anal-sadistic stage predominates, while the ego has achieved elevated modes that are not only fully developed but also culturally accepted. One may object that the animistic and magical tendency (superstition!) of the compulsive also indicates ego fixation at an earlier stage (Freud, Ferenczi). To this we rejoin that, from the standpoint of the total personality, only a *partial fixation of the ego occurs,* whereas in our patient's case the entire ego remained fixated at a primitive level.

But what does this total fixation look like and of what does it consist? We note that the hallmark of our case is the enormous discrepancy between ego and ego ideal. The mother is fully represented in the superego, while the ego remains sharply separate—infantile, weak, and ravaged by incest wishes. Normally, the child's ego adapts to the environment by incorporating fragments of it in the form of a superego, a process involving reaction formation and sublimation. The child's development is a gradual one: the external world of reality is incorporated bit by bit in the form of superego demands and is *most intimately blended with the existing ego.* In part, these demands are modified and molded to the individual ego structure, and the ebullient impulse ego must and does modify itself by means of compromise.

In the analysis of normals or mild neurotics, we cannot trace the formation of the ego ideal back to specific identifications;

should we manage to do so, we find the ego ideal in the most diverse and complex relationships—or better, "soldered"—to the sexual and other aspects of the ego. The more we trace the spectrum from the normal to the severely pathological, the clearer is the emergence of the *isolated superego,* and the more we recognize how crucial it is for psychic health *that the ego ideals harmonize organically with the burgeoning personality.*

The ego is made up of a series of identifications. It was created by a process of identification. Yet there must have been a "something" present which accomplished the identifications. This "something" could not have been anything other than a more primitive, differently constructed ego, an ego mainly composed of impulsive tendencies of a sexual and destructive nature. Freud has taught us to understand the complicated route this primitive impulse ego or pleasure ego must take if it is to develop into the ego of a normal adult. From the very outset, the impulse ego is thoroughly ambivalent toward the external world. Only the love for the nurturer impels one to deflect inwardly a portion of one's destructive drives and, normally, to set up "conscience" as a sublimated form of barrier. In so doing, one even learns to renounce a portion of his sensuous pleasure.

Now the environment plays a crucial role in *how* successfully these demands are incorporated. As noted in chapter 3, there are two possible ways for the process of identification to become pathological:

1. At the very outset, can the impulse ego oppose the restriction of pleasure, which would mean resisting identification with the forbidding nurturer? This it always does according to its nature as a pleasure ego. The strength of the resistance will then depend upon the intensity of the autoerotic organ pleasure experienced. The more intense the organ pleasure and the earlier it was effectively felt, the harder it is to set up a negating ego ideal. Of course, constitutional factors (of a hormonal nature?) will heavily influence this process.

2. Is the ambivalence toward the dominant nurturer so strong that each identification will be resisted by a counterstruggle of equal intensity? Identification born of ambivalence becomes clearer if we recall that positive object love must produce the identification. A child will more easily accept a prohibition

if it is done "for love of" the cherished object. In the final outcome, the "for love of" part will drop away, and the prohibition remains as an ego-ideal demand. But whenever stubbornness or a negative attitude of the same intensity competes with the "for love of," the prohibition will indeed take effect; but, at the same time, it will remain isolated. *This isolation can be tantamount to a repression.* The prohibition, then, will be impulsive, like a repressed sexual wish. It will try to become effective because of the consummated identification, but the pleasure ego, swayed by the negative attitude, slows it down and prevents its becoming an organic part of the total personality. This must generate a conflict within the ego which in every way is tantamount to the conflict in sexual repression. (The relationship between "isolation" and "repression of the super-ego" will be discussed later.)

Let us try now to apply to our case the theoretical concept of an "isolated superego." All along, what gave the patient's character its specific imprint was the acute, intense ambivalence toward the mother. The positive pole was produced by an oral fixation to the mother's breast and womb. She does not want any part of adulthood; she is not twenty-six, but two years old. She is rejected, condemned, and cursed by the mother and will not rest until the mother accepts her again. The wish to suckle the mother's breast was fully conscious.

The negative pole of the ambivalence is grounded in an unbridled devotion to incest-tinged objects. Up until the time of analysis, only the father image had undergone the most stringent repression. At age three, the poorly supervised child had engaged in rough sex play with her brothers and other boys. One day the mother's harsh prohibition suddenly materialized: the children were caught in the act and the patient severely beaten. The mother's beating and scolding ("You are a dirty whore," and so on) only served to intensify the sense of guilt. However, the child's stubborn, negative attitude, buttressed by the sexual pleasure she had felt, prevented the mother's veto from overriding the fully lived-out impulsive activity. The ego, then, is handicapped in its development, since the motherly ideal ("You must not play around sexually") is accepted but not integrated into the rest of the personality. The ego remains infantile at the stage of identification with the pleasure-giving genital and is doomed to battle with the harshly negative superego which it has incorporated. The formula of the never-ending fight differs from that of our other cases—"Though I want to, I must not masturbate or desire my father, etc."; rather, it reads, *"I must die as a penalty for the pleasure I feel from masturbation and intercourse."* This culminates in the symptom of genital masochism.

"Isolation of the superego" also implies a special structural organization of the personality, the genesis of which can perhaps be traced in part. We shall shortly tie in this structural peculiarity with economic and dynamic aspects. Some aspect of the personality structure is involved whenever we state that the impulsive's superego is not "organically" fused with the ego, as it is in the impulse-inhibited neurotic; rather, it is separated and isolated from it. *Dynamically,* this leads to a breakdown of the superego as an agent of repression and reaction formation and to the evolution of the unbridled impulse as a "crime born of a sense of guilt" (Freud). The isolated superego functions as a repressed impulse and creates the need for punishment, which largely seeks gratification in an undisguised masochistic form. This gives rise to the economic aspects of such an interplay. The unbridled impulse may, secondarily, even serve to discharge the feeling of guilt as a pathological means of gratifying the need for punishment. But we must beware of overestimating this very basic economic motive since it is in itself only secondary. The primary motive stems from the fact that the original organ pleasure holds an undisputed position, which, in such a personality structure, can be experienced even without manifest guilt feelings.[62]

However, we cannot ascribe the impulsive behavior primarily to the need for punishment, even if we consider how largely the "crime-born-of-guilt" mechanism figures in the sadistic type of impulsive, and [how predominant] self-punishment [is] in the masochistic. This is because almost every case of impulse-inhibited neurosis also shows a need for punishment: here the illness itself serves to gratify the masochistic demand for punishment. Whenever a scoundrel rationalizes his guilt feelings by tormenting those around him, or an impulse-laden masochist gets himself roundly punished, we are dealing with the type of ego dissociation discussed above. While the need for punishment is outspoken in the impulsive character, it is not specific to him.

An interesting variant of the impulsive character appeared in another patient of mine. From earliest childhood to the age of twenty-two, her ambivalence kept her in perpetual conflict with her parents. She lied, deliberately misbehaved, ran away from home, ran around with boys, and repeatedly beat up her mother without any qualms; she would also masturbate and experienced a number of "rapes" without ever having actual intercourse. Only the latter gave her enormous anxiety. She also suffered anxiety attacks and occasional insomnia. At age twenty-two, she finally surrendered to someone who was a father image to her. At this point, guilt feelings broke through. The mother threw her out and she fled to Vienna, where she experienced an attack of hysterical vomiting and gastric pains. Twice she underwent unwarranted laparotomy because the doctors suspected cardiospasm and did not recognize the functional nature of her symptoms. All of a sudden, the impulsive behavior slackened; the patient became quiet and depressed and began to invoke situations which replayed the maternal rejection in every detail. Even in analysis, she behaved in this manner. Before the onset of symptoms, she had resisted accepting her superego. It was only after intercourse had gratified her incest wish that the hitherto isolated ego ideal made itself felt as a repressing agent: it slowed down the impulsive behavior and created a symptom neurosis. (The vomiting and gastric pains corresponded to pregnancy fantasies.)

Let us compare such cases to the uninhibited impulsives, with particular emphasis on those who show, along with their impulsive behavior, symptoms of effective repression, such as anxiety, compulsive rumination, and phobias. We quickly recognize that acute ambivalence toward the nurturer does not always lead to pathological isolation of the ego ideal. Another possibility then presents itself: the nurturer's attitude, which is the blueprint for the child's ego ideal, does not oppose the original impulsive behavior but, on the contrary, fully sanctions it. In psychoanalysis, we often underestimate the importance of a defective model for the ego ideal. Aichhorn (loc. cit.) has shown that often such individuals were born out of wedlock, grew up fatherless, or were orphaned at a very early age. But it is not clear why such children did not borrow their ego ideals from other caretakers or why they are so constantly erratic in exercising self-restraint. It would be of great value to ascertain whether and to what degree a constant change of nurturers weakens the defensive mechanisms. One might readily postulate that frequent changes in child-rearing practices produce a fragmentation and disorganization of ego ideals.

Such a clash of diverse ego ideals was shown by a twenty-eight-year-old patient sent to the clinic by the Vienna Welfare Department for hysterical mutism. She also showed enormous anxiety, as evidenced by startle-prone behavior, defensive arm gestures, and sudden flight movements. The mutism represented an hysterical defense against carrying out a compulsive impulse. The patient lived with her three children in severe financial straits on a ridiculously meager income earned as a seamstress. She therefore decided to kill herself and her children. She failed to follow through because of the crying and screaming of her youngest child, a two-year-old girl. She then developed an impulse to blurt out compulsively what she had decided to do but feared that in so doing she would wind up in a psychiatric ward. (The patient had already been hospitalized for a suicide attempt.) Hence the patient's silence was a defense against carrying out the compulsive impulse. The attack of mutism occurred one night following a nightmare: she dreamt that the second oldest child was already dead. She had been pregnant with this child when her first husband was killed. At that time, she had cursed the child in her belly and thought it would be better off dead.

The patient had been twice married: the first husband died in an accident; she divorced her second husband because he drank too much and abused her. It is noteworthy that the patient was totally frigid despite her many love affairs.

It soon became apparent that the patient's murderous impulses, which she condemned, did not stop at the children. In addition, she premeditated crimes that were fully conscious, without self-recrimination, and therefore not compulsive in nature. For example, intent on poisoning her father-in-law, she made the acquaintance of a druggist who, however, refused to furnish her with the poison. During her three weeks of analysis, she would waylay me at my doorstep to "cool down" her rage at me and to "at least tear out a few hairs" of mine. She tried to obtain a revolver to shoot me. She thought—with full awareness—that it would be a great idea to castrate her doctor and her father-in-law. She gleefully gave in to her py-romaniac impulses without any qualms. At home, she burned everything she could get her hands on. She beat her child with a burning torch. At age ten, she had burned down a hay-stack to get revenge on the owner, who had scolded her. Also at age ten, she set fire to a neighboring house and endangered almost the whole village. She rejoiced when "others" were fearful; they should suffer too, not she alone.

Her childhood was merciless. She was born out of wedlock, put in an orphanage by the mother, and "educated" there for four years. She then came to live with a distant relative who systematically taught her to steal along with other children. In addition, there were always beatings. She slept with eight other people, some of them adults, in a small, confined room. Not only did she witness the most intimate sexual activities, but was even raped by her uncle and a young man. She did not steal willingly, but only because she was freezing! She hated her surroundings, but only because she was beaten. She took revenge whenever she could. She was malicious, insti-gated all kinds of mischief in school, which she attended only infrequently, took great pleasure in beating up the boys and tormenting the teachers, and, finally, in setting a fire. (She was enuretic to age twelve.)

When she was twelve years old, the new director of the school took an interest in her, removed her from the home, and became influential in her life. He taught her how to read and understand what she read, and wanted to educate her at his own expense. But the relative took her away, and the old way of life began all over again. Now, for the first time, she experienced anxiety states and tried to put a brake on her impulses, but was only partially successful.

Her hatred toward her oppressors grew immeasurably, but at the same time the director's influence became operational. *Her hatred collided with countercurrents, corresponding to the newly acquired superego, the good director.* She bought herself books, read a great deal, acquired some education and a relatively good writing style. I had occasion to read some letters that she wrote from Steinhof.

At the age of fourteen, she came to know her mother, who took her to live in the city. Here the life of misery and privation continued unabated. The old impulses were as lively as ever but partially braked. She tormented her first husband relentlessly and without remorse. After his death, she blamed herself (suicide attempt, hospitalization) and went through a phase of mounting agitation to the point of being delusional. She believed that her husband was still alive and was following her through the streets. She attempted new relationships, which ended unhappily. She could not endure staying with her second husband. Finally, she became unable to work and made a decision to die with the children.

Analytic treatment in the out-patient clinic was not feasible because of her dangerous actions. Therefore, we could not get an analytic history of her sexual development. Clearly evident, however, was the strong contrast between her failure to develop a culturally effective superego up to the age of twelve and the director's influence upon her. Now, for the first time, she put a curb on her impulses, albeit without much success, and at the same time acquired a sense of guilt, which was superimposed upon her fear of being beaten. The uninhibited impulsivity was partly curbed by the late but intensely incorporated superego and led into neurotic pathways. It was not strong enough to do the whole job of repression only because it became operational too late. We are using the term "repression" here in its loosest sense. However, there is no doubt that our patient's frigidity, for instance, corresponded to a repressed penis wish, even though conscious castration wishes existed. And we must wonder what happened as a result of her repressing the masculinity wish, though we cannot reach any definite conclusion.

But we must not overlook the fact that the patient was beaten, and we may assume that a phylogenetic readiness for repression or for guilt feelings could make use of this "educational" method as a means of developing repression. She was assaulted by her stepfather; she resisted it and brought upon herself a rejection by the male; yet, in her adult life, though totally frigid, she made neurotic attempts at establishing relationships. Was there only hatred operating in the child, was the resistance real because she had never experienced tenderness, or was she repressing a deep masochistic love? Even these questions we cannot resolve.

We should not look for a sharp contrast between this patient and our genital masochist. It seems to make no difference whether one acquires a culturally valid superego at age twelve or age four. The decisive factor will be the striking of a happy balance between pleasure gratification and impulse inhibition, a difficult achievement from birth to adulthood. Every inconsistency in the form of a suddenly imposed harshness must lead to malformations of the ego; these will approximate to a greater or lesser degree the most blatant form of the isolated (or repressed) superego, described above. But there doubtless exist still other typical ego defects.

The Problem of Superego Repression

We may deal with a possible objection by expanding on the structural and dynamic differences between the obsessional neurotic, the hysteric, and the impulsive character. Both the compulsive and the hysteric tend to pit their ego against the brutal severity of the superego. Freud comments on this as follows:

> In certain forms of obsessional neurosis, the sense of guilt is over-noisy but cannot justify itself to the ego. Consequently, the patient's ego rebels against the imputation of guilt and seeks the physician's support in repudiating it.... Analysis eventually shows that the superego is being influenced by processes *that have remained unknown to the ego.*[62] It is possible to discover the repressed impulses which are really at the bottom of the sense of guilt. Thus in this case the superego knew more than the ego about the unconscious id.[63]

The difference between the impulsive and the compulsive is clear: despite its battle with the superego, the ego [of the compulsive] knows nothing about the repressed material (in contrast to the impulsive character) and it behaves somewhat like an angry slave rebelling inwardly against his master's brutality while doing his duty despite the rebellion. The ego of the impulsive perpetrates open and conscious rebellion. Thus the rebellion succeeds in the latter but not in the former, because the impulse-inhibited compulsive was successful at reaction formation (more about this below), that is, he fully incorporated the forbidding figure into his ego, though rebelling against it later on; the impulsive identifies with only a part of his ego and never wholly completes the process of identification.

Hysteria cases are different and more complicated. As Freud

notes, the feeling of guilt remains unconscious:

> Here the mechanism by which the sense of guilt remains unconscious is easy to discover. The hysterical ego fends off a distressing perception with which the criticisms of its superego threaten it, in the same way in which it is in the habit of fending off an unendurable object-cathexis—by an act of repression. It is the ego, therefore, that is responsible for the sense of guilt remaining unconscious. We know that as a rule the ego carries out repressions in the service and at the behest of its superego; but this is a case in which it has turned the same weapon against its harsh taskmaster. In obsessional neurosis, as we know, the phenomena of reaction-formation predominates; *but here [in hysteria] the ego succeeds only in keeping at a distance the material to which the sense of guilt refers.* [64]

Thus, the ego of the impulse-inhibited hysteric represses id impulses in obedience to the superego, whose demands it has *unconsciously accepted*;[65] but, at the same time, it reacts to the severe threat by a systematic repression of guilt feelings, which we must analytically unravel from the anxiety and conversion symptoms. Thus every case of impulse-inhibited hysteria and obsessional neurosis shows an unconscious acceptance of prohibiting superego demands. They differ from one another in the particular attitude of the ego toward the sense of guilt. However, what mainly concerns us here is the matter of *repression of the superego*, for we must clarify the relationship between repression and isolation. As noted earlier, the isolation is equivalent to an act of repression: the superego then behaves like an impulse breaking through the repression.

On closer scrutiny, we at once hit upon a valid objection: are not the core demands of the superego always unconscious? For example, can the prohibition of incest ever become conscious? Would this not make the incest wish conscious? This intimate network of wish and prohibition condemns both to unconsciousness; as a problem in *The Ego and the Id*, it laid the groundwork for the theory that a portion of the ego—the superego—must of necessity remain unconscious.

But "unconscious" does not mean "repressed." The question becomes clear if we go strictly according to Freud's differentiation between the dynamic and systematic (system *ucs.*) and between successful and abortive repression. Only the unsuccessful dynamic repression is pathogenic. In healthy individuals and impulse-inhibited neurotics, the superego's core is always under successful systematic repression. The dynamic aspect of the repression does not overcome the coming-into-consciousness barrier, and the systematic repression is compatible with the ego's unconscious acceptance and performance of the superego's demands. Indeed, unconsciousness seems to be a prerequisite for acceptance. For, obviously, in the infantile type of impulsive, one often finds that the basic superego demand (incest prohibition) is conscious.[66] (This is especially true in the case of schizophrenics.) *The systematic repression is lacking here, while the dynamic repression turns out to be very strong and unsuccessful.* The following is clearer now, I believe: in the *impulse-inhibited neurotic*, a successful and systematic repression of the superego core is present and the dynamic repression does not overcome the coming-into-consciousness barrier.

The ego may know nothing of the superego's core; it knows only its own rationalizations, but it submits to the superego's demand to repress the id strivings. We know that the failure of this repression gives rise to symptoms. In the impulse-inhibited symptom neurosis, *the psychic conflict is played out between the ego plus superego on the one hand and the repressed part of the id (the tabooed object relations) on the other.*

In the impulsive character, repression by the superego is "dynamic" and "unsuccessful"; systematic repression is lacking. It is easy to grasp that the lack of systematic repression stems from the dynamic repression of the superego by the pleasure ego. (This also applies to the partial drives and to sadism.)

The psychic conflict unfolds here on three levels. On the one hand, the ego defends itself against the id in the service of the superego (the same occurs in an impulse-inhibited neurotic); on the other hand, the ego defends itself against the superego in the service of the id. This dual battle (dual counter-cathexes) gives rise to the overriding disorganization of the impulsive character.

Thus isolation of the superego implies unsuccessful dynamic repression, and more. It entails, above all, a special structural organization of the personality, and further (to be detailed later on), a normal "transitional" stage of each superego formation. We may justify the coining of a new term in that we are dealing here with a special case of repression of the superego. Someday the idea of "isolation" may be absorbed by the concept "repression of the superego," when the theory of dynamic "ego repression" is propounded (as an appendage to the theory of sexual repression) and the relationship to personality structure is understood.

The Isolation of the Superego as a Normal Transitional Phase in Ego Development

At this point, we must deal with a further objection. Genetically we can trace the isolation of the superego back to the child's ambivalence toward its object, from which the superego derives later on, and we consider this maldevelopment a specific attribute of the impulsive character (in contrast to the impulse-inhibited, classical obsessional neurosis). But it is precisely in the obsessive compulsive that ambivalence operates as a central factor and stands at the root of so many symptoms, such as doubting, indecision, and the like. Why is it that the ambivalence here did not give rise to isolation of the superego? The compulsive is especially noteworthy for his far-reaching fulfillment of the negative ego-ideal demands, for example, pedantry, meticulousness, sexual abstinence, a penchant for ascetic ideologies, and so on. We can easily override this objection by considering that the form of the ambivalence is crucial, that is, the manner in which it is manifest and the stage of psychic development at which it becomes operational. As for the latter point, I am referring to the distinction between the two forms of illness discussed in the previous chapter. As for the way the ambivalence is manifested, we should note the following:

1. The emotionally ambivalent attitude may express itself continuously *(manifest ambivalence).*

It may undergo polarization toward love or hate. In analysis, we are acquainted with the phenomenon first described by Freud and designated as *reactive love or reactive hate (latent ambivalence).* In the former case, hate transformed into love is superimposed upon the original love attitude; in the latter, love transformed into hate through disappointment is superimposed upon the original attitude of hate. The compulsive typically expresses manifest ambivalence in symptoms mostly attached to trivial matters; the original, ambivalently cathected object receives either his reactive love or reactive hate. The ambivalence toward the object only becomes manifest in analysis. The impulsive character keeps the manifest ambivalence toward the object and maintains this attitude toward the ego ideal, as explained. The original manifest ambivalence of the compulsive undergoes a modification, which is missing or deficient in the pure impulse disorder: the reactive accentuation of one pole of the ambivalence and the displacement [of the emotion] onto trivial matters. This reactive change of the ambivalence to a manifest love or hate occurs through repression, which we know is defective in the impulsive character. Even the compulsive's repression and reaction formation may be traced back to the harsh rigidity of the negating ego ideal. The impulsive constellation—defective repression, defective reaction formation, perpetuation of the manifest ambivalence, and isolation of the superego—is quite consistent.

A schematic representation of the extreme types may serve to clarify the differences:

Compulsion Neurosis

1. Manifest ambivalence.
2. Reactive modification of ambivalence.
3. Severe superego, built into the ego.
4. Strong repression and reaction formation.
5. Sadistic impulses combined with feelings of guilt.
6. Character is overconscientious; ascetic ideologies.
7. The ego subordinates itself to the superego.

Impulsive Character

1. Manifest ambivalence.
2. No reactive modification or hate predominates.
3. Isolated superego.
4. Defective repression.
5. Sadistic impulses without guilt feelings.
6. Character is unscrupulous; manifest sexuality with corresponding guilt feelings possibly linked to neurotic symptoms or totally repressed.
7. The ego remains ambivalent; straddles the fence between pleasure ego and superego, a factitious adherence to both sides.

Item 2 marks the dichotomy in development between an obsessional neurotic (or other symptom neurotic) and an impulsive character. The further direction taken now depends on the experiences occurring up to the anal stage. If the ambivalence first unfolds at this point, and there are no defects in prior stages, obsessional neurosis (or hysteria) will develop. If well-defined feelings of ambivalence already exist from earlier stages, reaction formation and incorporation of the ego ideal will fail. In line with our earlier discussion, premature sexual activity, particularly the *activation of genitality prior to completion of the oedipal phase,* tends to reinforce the narcissism of the primitive pleasure ego to such a degree that only isolated forms of ego ideals will be evolved. A further decisive factor is the sum total of defects in the love objects and nurturers, which we dwelt on earlier at length.

It is not my intention here to detail further the pathological development of the ego and the ego ideal, as it is already set forth in our discussion of the impulsive character. Genetic ego psychology, inaugurated by Freud and Ferenczi,[67] will probably have to deal with characteristic "stages of ego development" analogous to the already established stages of sexual development. But whenever an isolated ego ideal appears, we may recognize it as the pathological prolongation of a phase through which, presumably, everyone must pass in his evolution from a primitive pleasure ego to a member of civilized society. The civilized reality ego is built upon the model of the ego ideal only through fulfillment of some of the latter's aspects.[68] A large part of the ego ideal may always remain unrealized, and psychoanalysis can give us good insight into the pathological results of faulty fulfillment. The acquisition of the ego ideal does not proceed without a struggle. It is in the nature of the impulsive pleasure ego to defend itself against the nurturers' restrictions. Object love paralyzes this defense and thus potentiates the building of an ego ideal. However, between total resistance and genuine acceptance, a phase of acute, *manifest ambivalence* toward the frustrating object intervenes.

There are two possible sequelae: the manifest ambivalence changes to latent ambivalence through the reactive emphasis of love or hate; or the ambivalence toward the object or the ego ideal is overcome. The latter possibility we consider normal and strive for it in the analytic therapy of every single case. Clearly, the ambivalence within the ego yields only when the ambivalence toward the sexual object is overcome *(attainment of the unambivalent genital stage).* The compulsive and the hysteric typify the first possibility and can be schematized as follows:

1. *Stage of the primitive pleasure ego*: overt defense against restrictions.

2. *Stage of manifest ambivalent object cathexis, or, in the context of the superego, ambivalent attitude toward the superego*: fixation at this stage gives rise to the abiding fixation of an *isolated* superego and a tendency toward unbridled impulsivity, as discussed above.

3. *Stage of reactive modification of the ambivalence*: the ego identifies with the frustrating educator *(realization of the latter's demands on an ambivalent basis).* This is the starting point for the faulty identifications.[69] If it occurs at the anal-sadistic stage, the tendency is toward obsessional neurosis; if it becomes fixated at the genital stage, it predisposes to hysteria.

4. *Stage of (relatively) ambivalence-free ego structure*: no matter how obscure the genesis and dynamics, analytic experience affirms that this reality-oriented ego position cannot occur without the existence of impulse-affirmative elements within the ego ideal, that is, without the possibility of an orderly libido economy.[70]

This outline can serve only as a preliminary orientation. We may add that stages 1 to 3 must be accommodated to every phase of libidinal development, since the struggle between pleasure-striving and denial unfolds anew at every sexual stage. We can differentiate the impulsives from the compulsives and hysterics according to whether the phase of the isolated ego ideal became fixated at the anal-sadistic or genital stage.

One may object that the attempt to differentiate the unfolding of such phases in cross- and longitudinal section must remain mere speculation, since we can never accurately reconstruct the child's attitude through the fifth year of life. Whoever invokes the analytical reconstruction of childhood will be right to a certain extent, especially if we demur that the firmest part of Freudian theory, the stages of libidinal development, originated in this way and everyone can prove to himself its correctness, that is, the precise succession of oral, oral-sadistic, anal-sadistic, and genital stages. Yet our scheme of the developmental stages of the superego is based only minimally upon analytic reconstruction; it rests much more upon experiences gained in the treatment of impulsive characters, especially the analysis of their ambivalence conflicts and transference attitudes. During analysis, they continually change their superego structure in accordance with their transference feelings. This exactly replicates their early object relations and enables us—more clear-sightedly since the publication of *The Ego and the Id*—to gain a deeper insight into the evolution of the infantile ego.

We conclude this section with reference to a broader problem: self-love ("secondary narcissism" in the sense of Freud and Tausk) and object love are *life-affirmative* (love-impulse) elements in man, while feelings of guilt (need for punishment) are *life-negative* (death-impulse) elements. They bear an antithetical relationship to one another. Sometimes the sense of guilt transforms the self-love into a more primitive form of narcissism, into the primary narcissism of the womb situation. The most typical model for this fusion is suicide in the melancholic. The sense of guilt is ontogenetically later than the narcissism; hence the triumph of the life-affirmative tendency. A fully developed narcissism, maintained by unambivalent genitality, works best against the feeling of guilt. A person's later fate most crucially depends upon *the phase of narcissistic development at which an effective sense of guilt makes its appearance, thereby weakening the life-affirmative tendency.* The severity of an illness seems to depend upon how early the sense of guilt initiated its life-negating and reality-negating effect. We may number such homeostatic problems among the most difficult to grasp empirically and count them among the core problems in the specific etiology of psychic illness.

6. Schizophrenic Projection and Hysterical Dissociation: Some Observations

Our postulate of an isolated superego has doubly proven itself of heuristic value—for formulating the dynamics of schizophrenic projection, and of hysterical dissociation as well.

When our genital masochist learned of the death of the woman doctor who first treated her and who had become a total mother image to her, she experienced an acute hysterical psychotic break. She had auditory and visual hallucinations in which "Mami" would knock on her door at night and summon her to her grave. During a session, she saw "Mami" lying in her grave waving to her. She heard voices telling her not to masturbate—"Mami" wouldn't allow it. For hours she prayed tearfully before the dead woman's picture and saw it move. We have good grounds for attributing these hallucinations to the same mechanism as operates in schizophrenic projection. The same process of projection occurs here as in the latter during a developmental stage of the ego. The ego ideal manifests itself externally (like the pursuer and critic in paranoid schizophrenia). Or, better put, it *re*appears in the external world and the process of introjection ceases. Thus, *most susceptible to the fate of paranoid shift from ego to outside world are those parts of the personality, those ego ideals, that once were not wholly fused with the total personality but remained estranged from it.* Nor is this assumption negated by the fact that the content of the projection—be it delusions of persecution or paranoid hallucination—is also the impulse (mainly homosexual) condemned by the ego ideal. The patient then behaves like an innkeeper with two guests quarreling at his door—whatever happens, he must put up with the clamor. The clinical manifestation of resistance likewise contains both—the repressor and the repressed.

We would thereby partly solve the problem so perpetually tied to Freud's hypothesis about paranoid projection in homosexuality. From the economic viewpoint, the process of projection was explained as an attempt at discharge: I do not love him—in fact I hate him because he is persecuting me."[71] But this economic interpretation failed to explain why the paranoid schizophrenic tries to relieve his impulses only through projection and not, for example, by evoking typical mechanisms of repression. We may now postulate that a defect within the ego facilitates projection and directs the forbidden impulse into this specific avenue of discharge. A defect in ego development such as incomplete fusion of ego ideals *derived from the external world* would predispose toward psychotic projection *into the external world.* As to the nature of this defect and its timing for effecting such a tendency, we learn nothing from examining the paranoid forms of schizophrenia itself. The ambivalent nature of every persecution complex clearly points up the key role of ambivalence here. The mere analysis of a paranoid neurotic character suggests the assumption of this fixation point. But if we are right about the genesis of this tendency, we have also gained some clues as to the time of the schizophrenic fixation—and we believe that an hypothesis is legitimate as long as it can explain data.

In one of his lectures, Schilder pointed out the loosening of the ego ideals in schizophrenia and used this, among other factors, to explain even the conscious awareness of symbolic meanings [which such cases show]. He also raised the question as to the timing of the schizophrenic fixation but did not answer it. One train of thought which runs parallel to this work and is intimately related to it raises the question as to the genesis of formal disturbances of psychic life: it begins by challenging the incorrect assumption that we should localize the schizophrenic fixation stage in the same manner as that of melancholia (oral-sadistic), compulsion neurosis (anal-sadistic), and hysteria (genital). In dealing with the question of schizophrenic fixation, we must first strongly emphasize the formal disturbances which characterize it; secondly, we must not forget that schizophrenia can mimic all types of psychic illness (altered in form)—compulsion neurosis, hysteria, melancholia, hypochondria, etc.; thirdly, the assumption of a narcissistic fixation is much too broad to mean anything specific. In the final analysis, it will involve a *certain stage within the narcissistic autoerotic phase of development,* presumably when the first bridge is thrown from the inchoate ego to the object [world],[72] the earliest identifications are formed,[73] and the process of reality-testing is unfolding. The schizophrenic fixation must be sought in the stage of earliest object identification.

Hysterical dissociation of the personality is another way in which the ego can escape the role of mediator between superego and primitive tendencies (in contrast to the discharge of the superego through psychotic projection)—*double conscience* of Janet. Here there is no projection, no expulsion of the ego's enemies (which is, after all, a definite though always unsuccessful decision); rather, *the ego identifies first with one opponent and then another.* Thus, *during masturbation,* our nymphomaniac patient totally identified with the punitive mother, a maneuver we must construe as a special kind of hysterical "state of emergency," while her pleasure ego identified with her genital. *Outside of this emergency state,* she plays the role of the small child toward all persons in any way suitable to her purpose: she tries to cling to the doctor, the nurse, etc., but becomes very stubborn and temperamental when rebuffed. She involves herself in countless, always incest-tinged relationships and seeks in the male the father with the big penis. But if coitus occurs, the figure of the threatening mother intervenes, sometimes in the form of voices calling her a "dirty whore" and sometimes in the figure of the devil who condemns her.

A female hysteric with twilight states (to be discussed elsewhere in detail), who finally wound up with a permanently split personality, gave me the idea that the dissociation is an attempt at restitution. I was also persuaded of this on the basis of two other cases. In the prepsychotic twilight state, the patient relived an otherwise forgotten sexual assault by a teacher; at the same time, she masturbated on her breasts and dressed in her prettiest clothes, though normally she dressed very plainly. Thus, in the twilight states, her ego surrendered to the forbidden drives, which were fully repressed in the waking state, and accommodated them by bringing them to motor discharge. In the normal waking state, the ego subjugated itself to the severe, motherly superego, which had preached abstinence. In her second year of life, she had already suffered frustration of genital masturbation by her mother. It seems typical for such cases that the ego oscillates between the pole of the superego taboos and that of the impulses.

The ego serves two hostile masters; it loves both and would follow both. But the conflict is not solved through a compromise symptom [formation] as in the symptom neuroses; rather, the one is not allowed to know of the other's existence (dissociation into two states of consciousness). Even this case showed a clear-cut, sharp ambivalence toward the mother since early childhood, which we shall not elaborate any further. We only wish to mention that the positive tendency toward the mother was based upon an intense oral tie and longing for the womb, while the negative sprang primarily from genital frustration, which was experienced as extreme castration. This case therefore resembles our nymphomaniac patient, with one great difference—she never experienced full impulse gratification in early childhood. The culmination of the ego's ambivalence toward its ideal finally occurred through the patient's allowing the ego to die ("I have given Eva S., that is, myself, the kiss of death; I am not Eva S.; I am nameless"), and indeed what ego she had was identified with the pleasure ego. Stubbornness toward the mother dominated the child's attitude from the very beginning. Even at this point, we must note the tendency toward dissociation in a defective incorporation of the forbidding motherly ideal. The ambivalence is fully contained in the expression "kiss of death." The expulsion of the depressive, prepsychotic personality, with insight into the illness, at first triggered a hypomanic reaction. The patient lost her symptoms (insomnia and hysterical gastritis) and felt well.

In the psychotic phase, the patient told me she now knew much more about Eva S. than the latter would have known during her lifetime. What it was she did not wish to tell me. But we understand that she was now allowed to know more about the repressed material; after all, she had the delusion that it belonged not to her but to Eva S., to whom she had given the "kiss of death."

The tendency toward schizophrenic and hysterical dissociation can thus be traced back to a faulty merging of the accepted ego ideals and the pleasure ego. Still unanswered is the question as to how the two forms of dissociation differ.

We may roughly summarize the above as follows:

In schizophrenia of the delusional and hallucinating variety, there is a conflict and a disintegration within the ego. The former is disposed of through discharge by way of psychotic projection of the ego ideal along with the tabooed id striving.

In hysterical dissociation, the ego tries to solve its conflict by *successively* siding with each master.

In the impulsive character, there is a *simultaneous* siding with both; sometimes conflicts are solved through a type of schizophrenic projection or hysterical dissociation.

These clinical pictures with their ego dissociation stand in contrast to impulse-inhibited character neurotics and to symptom neurotics with their firmly fused ego (ego plus superego).

However, we do not mean to imply that there are no ego

conflicts in the impulse-inhibited neurotic. Such conflicts are surely present—for example, between opposing ego identifications. It all depends upon whether there is a weakening of the common united defense which they maintain against the repressor, a defense quite compatible with the existing ego conflict.

7. Therapeutic Pitfalls

Since its inception, psychoanalytic treatment has been steadily broadening its horizons in the realm of psychic illness. In the beginning, it was suitable only for curing hysteria; soon it drew even compulsion neurosis into its domain and proved to be the most adequate treatment modality for this ailment. Freud and Abraham had already attempted the treatment of melancholia and related cyclic states. The results are not definitive as yet. The same holds true for attempts with cases of incipient schizophrenia. Psychoanalytic literature shows no indication of potential or actual success in this regard,[74] but, here and there in analytic circles, they say we should not reject a priori the possibility of analytically influencing this severe form of mental illness. First, we must determine the exact conditions under which we can exert an influence in the future, for it is a basic tenet of psychoanalysis that we can change only what we understand.

However, in advanced, institutionalized cases of schizophrenia, these conditions will scarcely be found. At first, only incipient cases will qualify for this treatment, or at least those cases which are not full-blown but show, nonetheless, typical schizophrenic mechanisms coupled with a strong transference neurosis—that is, cases like our patient with the world destruction fantasies. Since the schizophrenic is presently unreachable—not only because he cannot establish a transference, but also because the ego ideal breaks down—the analysis of the impulsive character may well afford the opportunity to clarify the requisites of treatment and its pitfalls, to the extent that they typify them.

"Within every man lurks a child who wants to play." With these words, Nietzsche anticipated Freud's classical formulation of the neurotic conflict. In analysis, we appeal to the "man" while proceeding to tame the "child," the unconscious, the infantile, the opponent of reality-testing. Our therapeutic efforts fail if the man refuses to combat the child; we succeed if we can win over the man and motivate him to deal with the child—either to retrain it or allow it some measure of controlled freedom. In transference neuroses, the major part of the personality quickly allies with us and becomes identified with our therapeutic endeavors. Not so in the impulsive character. Even his ego has stayed more or less infantile. From this difference in psychological makeup come all the pitfalls of treating these patients analytically.

A first typical problem to confront us is the deficient or absent insight into illness. With the symptom neurotic, an awareness of illness brings him to analysis, and, before any transference takes place, he is generally committed to opening up to the analyst; the impulsive, however, is mainly without insight into his most basic disturbances. Even in the transference neurosis, insight at first pertains only to the troublesome symptoms; the patient is generally unaware of his neurotic character traits. But the symptoms provide welcome access to the pathological material, and the gaining of further insight is not unduly arduous. With impulsive characters, it is different. Their attitude is mainly suspicious. Sometimes they cannot be moved to talk at all. It may happen that we win the patient's trust at the first interview by taking his side at the outset and never preaching to him or mouthing his opponent's view; in that case, we may quickly determine whether the lack of insight goes very deep, as in overt schizophrenia, for example, or whether a sharp current conflict has pushed the patient into maintaining his homeostasis with hysterical attacks, crying fits, convulsive sobbing, paroxysms of rage, and the like. Since the patient's opponent is not necessarily a more insightful or flexible individual, but rather represents the view of the husband or father who rears her—severely neurotic himself most of the time—we have the groundwork laid for the rationale of her condition, and it would be a lost labor to fight against it. Mainly a change of environment, such as separation from the opponent, makes analysis possible, but this is usually hard to come by, especially among the poor. Insight into pathological phenomena, whether neurotic symptoms or character traits, can exist only when the ego allies itself with the superego, which sharply and successfully denies the impulse. But if the superego allies itself with the pathological attitude, or remains isolated, or if the symptom does not appear absurd or irrational to the patient, insight is lacking. Thus our patient with the world destruction fantasy was totally unaware of her attitude toward her mother, because her superego was borrowed from her father, who behaved in the same way. The superego of our genital masochist remained isolated from the reality ego ("You must die from masturbation"); therefore insight was lacking here also. Indeed, we occasionally find absence of insight even in patients with circumscribed hysterical symptoms. Thus a patient with hysterical vomiting, who was involved at the time in severe battles with her brother's wife, thought it entirely normal to throw up after getting upset.

The acquisition of insight comes about in diverse ways. One typical possibility is that a strong transference may lead to identification with the analyst and through this the poorly understood unbridled impulse is converted into a typical compulsive act. In the case of the genital masochist, whenever the most deeply repressed hatred of the mother became conscious, compliance with the mother's invective was lost during masturbation: the impulse to masturbate now appeared as a typical compulsive symptom laden with guilt feelings, self-condemnation, and anxiety attacks whenever she tried to suppress masturbation. In this phase, the punitive actions and invective against the genital stopped; she masturbated with heterosexual fantasies of coitus and corresponding feelings of guilt. The old ego ideal effected the condemnation in a new form.

The attitude change toward the symptom became even clearer in the patient with the world destruction fantasy. Because of unhappy experiences in similar cases, I bent over backward not to remind her by my attitude of her father or mother, which meant I refrained from any prohibition or any active intervention into her behavior. Had I done otherwise, I would have immediately reinforced an *insuperable* acute ambivalence toward myself. In the beginning, I confined myself, without further analysis (which, by the way was quite impossible), to making clear to her that her actions were all acts of revenge: she had had to suffer greatly from her parents; her older (prettier) sister was preferred to her, and now she was trying to turn the house upside down out of revenge. I held that she was entirely right but that she would destroy herself by fulfilling that right. At first, she presented the strongest defense reactions against me, but gradually the positive transference gained the upper hand to such an extent that she agreed to have a try at behaving herself at home. This she did only by dint of an incredible self-discipline—the mere attempt was taken as [a sign of] progress. After fourteen days, she flared up again. I now explained to her that her parents would forbid analysis if she would not keep quiet. (This assumption was justified.) By now, the transference was so strong that she feared termination of the analysis. *Only at this juncture did she feel the sadistic impulses toward her mother as a compulsion, and this was a painful realization for her.* She began to see the futility of her attitude. Her guilt feelings, which were tied to her world destruction fantasies, she now correctly related to her sadistic impulses. The situation became critical when her outer-directed sadistic urges were checked and turned against the self: she wanted to commit suicide.

This critical change at the emergence of insight appears to be typical in such cases. (I had a similar experience in two other cases.) *The patient gains insight into his aggressive actions toward the environment by rightly relating them to his guilt feelings, which are always stirring around somewhere at the same time; at this point, suicidal impulses break through.* Our patient verbalized the following: "I realize that I wanted to get my parents' attention and concern by acting crazy. I feel so inferior" (the rivalry with the older sister, existing since childhood); "if this is taken from me, what do I have left?" For a long time she could not relinquish these secondary gains from illness.

The change in the ego ideal ensues in the course of analysis of the basic object relations. If the original object is devalued—which is partly possible through intellectual working-out but mainly through a new relationship to the doctor—the old superego loses its dynamic footing. The acquisition of insight occurs more or less typically in the following states:

1. *Stage of absent insight*: the pathological reactions are

compatible with the effective superego, or isolation of the superego from the ego allows the full surrender of the latter to the impulsive strivings.

2. *Stage of the growing, positive transference*: the patient makes the doctor a libidinal object. Already, through this process, the old ideal is pushed down a step; any narcissistic libido connected to it is changed into object libido. The new object, the doctor, can provide the basis of new superego formation inasmuch as he stands for the reality principle and interprets the heretofore unperceived attitude as running counter to reality.

3. *Phase of effective insight*: a portion of the new—and, by the way, incestuously cathected—object, the doctor is introjected and becomes the new ego ideal; the old is renounced along with its source. Only now can regular analysis begin.

In the first phase, such patients transfer their attitudes and aggressive feelings immediately to the analytic situation; but hate, distrust, and ambivalence especially threaten to make every attempt at analysis an illusion. Distrust and ambivalence are also typical attributes of the compulsive. But, in the latter case, they operate only in connection with the analyst's rejection and are generally susceptible to analysis. In the impulsive character, they take effect through actions. The doctor becomes a bitterly hated enemy, and serious intent to kill him is present. The patient discussed in chapter 5 planned exactly how she would waylay me on the street and shoot me down. She had even been to a gun shop to buy a revolver.

Where the actions are dictated not by hatred, but by a longing for love, they likewise show all the hallmarks of a defective ego ideal. Love is frankly demanded; no insight comes from the analyst's attempts to remind the patient of the transference nature of such love. Only a struggle could keep our nymphomaniac patient from undressing or masturbating during a session. Another patient very quickly developed the unshakable hope that the doctor would begin an affair with her. After an explicit indication that this could never happen, she broke off analysis. One patient, who frankly demanded homosexual intercourse with me, became enraged at my rejection, kicked and thrashed about, and could hardly be quieted down. Such forms of transference are obviously inconceivable in transference neuroses and only become manifest as intimations of a tender nature;

sensual wishes must be unraveled from dreams or they are forthwith repudiated as soon as they have reached full consciousness.

Since such patients are generally involved in acute conflicts with parents or parent surrogates, and since they are generally people who have suffered severe repeated disappointments, they compulsively try to carry the conflict even into analysis. Insofar as neurotics live out this repetition compulsion in analysis within reasonable limits, one can even spare them disappointments. One can be more friendly and helpful, since they are used to it from their environment. But how can disappointment be avoided if the patient creates situations which must evoke the most emphatic reaction? The nymphomaniac cited so often as an example was brilliant at provoking me to severity. She would often declare she did not want to stop the session. Kindly persuasion was of no avail here. Only after being told that she would be thrown out would she leave, crying and often yelling that we were mean to her, nobody loved her, we were insulting her, and so on. In this way, she would live out the rejection in masochistic fashion and would masturbate with corresponding fantasies. Another patient came to realize after many months of difficult work that her only reason for coming late and behaving badly was her wish to have me beat her; she later frankly declared that she always knew this but wanted to test my patience just as she had done with her father. But his beating she had experienced as pleasurable.

Wherever there are criminal impulses, the strictest prohibitions with threats of breaking off the analysis must be invoked. One must generally work with a much stronger transference than usual if the aim is to curb the acting-out. Especially with masochistic patients, this Scylla stands face to face with the Charybdis of producing a fixation that often cannot be dissolved. According to my experience so far, in extreme cases we cannot even come close [to dissolving such a fixation]. We can counter this only somewhat through daily discussion of the transference, with heavy emphasis upon the hopelessness of gratifying the patient's desires.[75] In milder cases, the transition into the aforementioned third phase comes about rather easily. In patients who remain strongly infantile, one of the biggest obstacles is getting them to do the analytic work of association. They cannot or will not understand what is asked of them.[76] The work of association is also hampered by the constant acting-out. But if we do get them to associate, to produce ideas and flashes of insight, and if the memory work does get under way we hit upon a new obstacle.

For example: after more than a year of analytic labor, we succeeded in making the nymphomaniac patient capable of working. A six-week vacation break had a salutory effect in achieving a partial weaning from the doctor. The acting-out abated, and the memory work on repressed material proceeded fairly well for three weeks. The patient recalled incest wishes from her third and fourth year of life, which had hitherto been fully buried. Shortly thereafter, her father, an eighty-year-old with senile dementia, came to Vienna. The patient grew nervous, had intensified guilt feelings, and fantasized having intercourse with him. No matter how strong the fantasy, the following occurs typically, to a lesser degree, in the pronounced impulsive character: the tabooed wishes are not condemned after reaching consciousness, as occurs regularly in neurotics; they press for discharge. How far this prevails depends upon the amount of reinforcement of the ego ideal which could be evoked up to that point. Our theorem would therefore read: in cases involving a defect in the ego ideal, ego analysis is a must, above all. But in practice it is always more complicated, no matter how high-sounding and logical the theorems obtained in this way.

First of all, it so happens that currently we do not know what the so-called ego analysis should look like, and we doubt whether it should even be separated from the rest of analysis.[77] [We wonder] whether it would not entail [using] the most blunt persuasion without regard to causal factors and associations. Without kindly encouragement and persuasion, at least in the beginning, one can never manage in such cases. One must, *lege artis*, educate the patient in order to prepare him for the analysis. But we would only founder in deepest misunderstanding and only document our thorough ignorance of psychodynamics if we were to keep this introductory phase separate and counterpose it to analysis under the label of "psychagogy." One could object that, as we ourselves admit, the uncovering of repressed impulses in such cases would lead to a push for motor discharge and that therefore analysis would be contraindicated. Even we ourselves would gladly opt for pure education, if we could only be sure it could achieve what analysis cannot. The educational successes with antisocial subjects reported by Aichorn are indeed outstanding; however, in the first place, his antisocial individuals are not entirely identical to our impulsive characters, though they show many similarities. And secondly, no doctor, nor even institution, can afford the destruction of all the furniture for the sake of the abreactions. Third, everyone who has had to deal with such patients will admit that they are especially noteworthy for their inability to accept persuasion for any length of time (stubbornness). Therefore we maintain that educational intervention is always necessary to make possible an ensuing analysis. The question of how to avoid the pitfall of a breakthrough of impulse must be left open. Our experience is insufficient for a satisfactory solution. In general there is only one rule to follow: uncover the unconscious very carefully and slowly; indeed, slow down the process at times, particularly when schizophrenic mechanisms play a role.

Unfortunately, the only feasible way to get at socially dangerous impulsivity is blocked today: psychoanalytic treatment in an institution. With few exceptions, mental hospitals are only custodial in nature and exist for the protection of society. The patient himself is entirely secondary. If we follow the fate of such hospitalized patients, we can discern the following pattern: the patient is at first confined because of a suicide attempt; he is discharged but returns sooner or later and gradually develops a peculiar tie to the hospital. Each time, his impulses grow more threatening, more dangerous, until finally one suicide attempt is successful, or the patient remains permanently hospitalized as a "psychopath" or a schizophrenic.

Psychoanalysis has been able to show how extensively environmental factors, financial misery, parental ignorance and brutality, and surely even predisposition transform children into antisocial, sick, distorted human beings. Humanity protects itself from them by locking them up—which always makes for deterioration under present conditions. But if the "conscience of humanity should awaken one day" and wish to right the many wrongs done to these patients by so many of its representatives, surely psychoanalysis will be called to the front lines to collaborate in their liberation from neurotic misery—in a setting far more propitious than the conditions now prevailing.

The Basic Antithesis of Vegetative Life Functions*

1. Point of Departure and Basic Hypothesis

As disturbances in genitality became more crucial in the economic view of mental illness, I was still a long way from appreciating the far-reaching consequences which an understanding of the orgastic function would have in various fields.

Whereas before, genital disturbance was seen as a symptom that might or might not occur in a neurosis, I had definitely established that, in general, such disturbance was pathognomonic of and essential to the development of neurosis. I now had to pursue—within the clinical framework of research in neurosis—the relationship between mental illness and disturbances of natural sexual functioning.

The years following publication of *Die Funktion des Orgasmus* (1927) were devoted to a study of character problems. The psychic apparatus, in particular the ego, must deal with blocked sexual excitation; the means of dealing with this blockage is the basic problem of character formation. Further research on the sex-economic aspects of mental illness forced me back to the original starting point, the better to deal with the difficult problem of anxiety.

On the one hand, my revision of the orgasm theory[1] showed that it, first and foremost, was the logical continuation of Freud's original libido theory, and that it in no way contradicted the psychoanalytic theory of the neuroses. On the other hand, my work on the relationship between anxiety and sexuality was incompatible with the classical formulation of eros and death instinct, and definitely contradicted it, since (if correct) it did away with the basic assumptions of that theory.

In my opinion, sexual excitation and anxiety are antithetical

*Translated from "Der Urgegensatz des vegetativen Lebens," *Zeitschrift für Politische Psychologie und Sexualökonomie,* I, 1934.

functions of all living substance in general, and of the psychic apparatus in particular. It is this basic antithesis that gives rise, secondarily, to the other well-known antagonistic functions of the instinctual apparatus. Thus I equate every primary motor excitation, that is, every reaching out to the external world of objects, with the psychoanalytic concept of "libidinal drive." I doubt Freud's correctness in giving "libido" such a broad connotation, but would rather construe it simply as, life energy (though not in the old-fashioned Jungian sense of psychic monism). While Freud sees a hypothetical death instinct as antithetical to sexual (libidinal) excitation, I see *anxiety* as a *primary* irreducible tendency of the living organism. I base this on a *dialectic dualism* of living substance, in general, and of the psychic apparatus, in particular.

In addition to my revised theory of the instincts based on dialectic principles, I also see an identity of so-called functional and somatic processes. This view differs from the following three older views about the relationship of psyche and soma:

1. The soul (psyche) builds the body for itself; it is eternal, absolute, "primary" (metaphysical idealism).

2. The soul (psyche) is a secretion of the brain (vulgar mechanistic materialism).

3. Psyche and soma are two independent causal entities, mutually interrelated (psychophysical parallelism).

I see the dynamic interplay of psyche and soma as a *functional psychophysical identity*. It seems meaningless to speak of two separate autonomous processes which obey their own laws, or of a one-sided dependence of one upon the other. Rather, we will try to prove that the known, primary psychic and somatic functions are absolutely identical with regard to basic life processes, and that under certain circumstances they split into antithetical functions—so that we may speak of a functional antagonistic duality.

At this point, one may wonder about the usefulness of another formulation of the body-mind relationship when there are already so many around. I myself would have taken this attitude and refrained from pure speculation. However, in the course of studying basic sexual functions, I realized that the lack of clarity in this regard had led to typical errors in formulating its role in sexuality—including those of the psychoanalysts, who had hitherto given us our most complete insight into sexual matters. However, some basic clinical observations, described below, enabled us to break ground toward an understanding of that borderline territory between the psychic and the physical.

It may not be amiss to say a few words here about the way in which we dared approach this most sensitive of all fields. We start from the structure of the individual, as laid bare by psychoanalytic theory. According to the latter, the psychic apparatus is composed of three structures—interconnected, mutually interacting, and even partly overlapping in their origin. They are *id, ego,* and *superego.*[2] The superego is the representation of the external social reality (that is, of the existing social order whatever it may be) *within* the individual; the id is the sum total of all the given biological needs which, so to speak, "are rooted in somatic processes." The biological and social aspects of the individual are in conflict with regard to need gratification or denial: the basic conflict is that between need and external world. It is only within this context, according to psychoanalysis, that the psychic structures begin to emerge. The originally undifferentiated id "separates off a part of itself," namely, the ego, which takes over the function of perception and transforms the id impulses into orderly, coordinated activity. The ego, insofar as it serves these functions, is wholly on the side of the id. It is a "pleasure ego," which responds to the stimuli streaming in by differentiating the individual from the chaos of perceptions, both internal and external, and, on the basis of the pleasure and unpleasure it experiences, separates itself from the external world. Everything that is pleasurable becomes part of the enlarged pleasure ego. Everything that is unpleasurable is assigned to the external world. The phenomena of introjection and projection, of incorporation and dissociation (particularly in psychoses), can be traced to this phase of differentiation between id and external world, primarily to the nursing period where, according to unequivocal clinical findings, the mother's breast is incorporated into the pleasure ego. Probably, it is the final withdrawal of the breast that for the first time leaves behind strivings—out of the "narcissistic reservoir"—for pleasure objects of the external world (object libido).[3] Later the ego must mediate between the urgent needs of the id and the prohibitions of the outside world, as well as heed the latter; therefore, the ego, up to now only a part of the id, comes in conflict with the id, as the defender of outside interests. To begin with, however, this process is at the service of the ego, which wants to maintain itself. Thus, even very early in life, two tendencies arising from a common source come into conflict with each other: self-preservation, fear of "punishment," prevents the gratification of other needs of the id. At first, this occurs out of fear of punishment, failure, loss of love, and the like. Later the forbidding figures of the external world, or rather, certain of their qualities, are taken into the ego, "introjected," and from then on the ego limits its needs in response to an "inner morality." What was formerly anxiety or perceived as such, now becomes an inner conscience, equipped with the full force of an anxiety drive. From now on the ego remains as the mediator between biological needs and social demands.

With this brief summary of the psychic apparatus, it is easy to sort out the scientific areas of research in sex economy. Studying psychic structures and their relationship to one another is really the domain of clinical psychoanalysis. Questions pertaining to the superego lead to sociology as a theory of laws regulating social existence. If, however, we delve deeply into id and ego functions, especially id functions, and into instinctual sources, we arrive at physiological and biological questions. Here the psychological boundaries become blurred. Here we come upon clearer and more inevitable issues at the scientific core of psychology, which, in the last analysis, still elude understanding: for example, the *quantity* of excitations, whose interplay is the basic problem of psychodynamics; or the problem of how affect becomes linked to conceptionalization and perception; the transformation of sexual feeling into anxiety or hate, etc. Obviously, to understand the borderland between psyche and soma, we must begin with the nature of the drives and affects themselves. While biology and physiology go from physical phenomena to the more complex, "higher" psychic functions, psychoanalysis, by a process of reduction to the simplest laws, goes from complicated psychic phenomena to their sources, the drives. Sex economy continues this study into the field of physiology, since, as a science of sexual functioning, it cannot stop at the boundaries of the psychic realm, as psychoanalysis, because of its method, is forced to do. It seems obvious that physiological and psychological research *must* meet in certain problem fields if they proceed correctly. The meeting ground is that of the *vegetative nervous system*, with its relationship, on the one hand, to the basic biological functions, and, on the other, to psychic mechanisms.

We need to say a few words more about how sex economy assumes the right to step from sexual psychology into the physiological realm. Such attempts by psychoanalysts like Ferenczi, F. Deutsch, and Groddeck, among others, suffer from the fact that the psychoanalytic *method of interpretation of meaning and association* was carried over to the physiological field. Thus, they tried to find a "psychic meaning" in the sex act, that is, to make the sex act an expression of some third entity, analogous to a psychic phenomenon—for example, a regression to the mother's womb (Ferenczi, Groddeck). A number of years ago, I had already tried to show that basic physiological functions could not be interpreted psychologically. Only the *disturbances* of such functions could be psychogenic.

There is, however, another way of going from psychology to physiology without carrying over into the physiological realm laws which are valid only psychologically. Dialectic observation teaches us that the psychic apparatus has a biophysical origin and that, therefore, two kinds of laws must be invoked. The first set of laws should deal with the psychic apparatus in terms of what it shares in common with this biophysical origin—such as tension and discharge, stimulus response, etc.; the second set of laws should deal with those features which differentiate the psychic from the physiological, which are solely its own and, therefore, antithetical to the physiological. In this category, for example, are repression of instinctual drives, introjection, projection, identification, etc. Without this clear distinction between psychophysical identity and antithesis—and if one applies psychological laws to physiological phenomena, as did Groddeck—errors result. But since the psychic apparatus is also a part of the biophysical apparatus, certain laws pertaining to the former must also govern the latter. This applies especially to the law of tension and discharge. Only with the aid of laws *in common,* first discovered in the psychic realm, can we make progress in physiological problems as well.

The following will show to what extent this is useful.

2. Sexual Excitation and Anxiety

The Problem of Anxiety

In 1895, Freud noted that patients with functional heart symptoms or acute anxiety states also showed characteristic disturbances in their sexual life; "free-floating anxiety" appeared whenever sexual excitation did not culminate in satisfaction, and especially often when intercourse was interrupted. From these facts, Freud correctly concluded that sexual excitation which is denied motility and the chance to become conscious must necessarily change into anxiety, since the latter appears in place of, and does away with, the sexual excitation. On the basis of these findings, he differentiated between "anxiety neurosis" and "anxiety hysteria"; in the latter, the anxiety is no longer "free-floating" but is bound to certain ideas. In such a case, it is assumed that the anxiety stemming from dammed-up sexual excitation becomes symptomatically "bound" (as, for example, in a compulsive symptom). In analyzing such a symptom, we break it up into its components by uncovering its latent psychic content or by preventing its expression (as, for example, when we stop a compulsive ritual). Anxiety then appears in place of the symptom, a process which may be regarded as the binding up of otherwise free anxiety into a symptom.

The original concept—that blocked sexual excitation turns into anxiety—was later set aside by Freud as unimportant, and anxiety was conceived mainly as a "signal" of the ego at the threat of danger. Yet the question remained as to how the ego "can give a signal," and it seemed important to find out the nature of the excitation in this process.[4]

Let us start by orienting ourselves in the complex realm of psychic anxiety. Our point of departure is the basic formula worked out by psychoanalysis. When one is threatened by a real external danger, such as a traffic collision or an attack by a dog, a state of anxiety ensues; the same thing occurs when certain patients, that is, anxiety hysterics and phobics, fantasize compulsively, without basis in fact, that a beloved person might meet with an accident. The first kind of anxiety, rationally based, we call *reality anxiety*; the second, irrational in nature, we call *neurotic anxiety*. Analytic delving into the latter shows that it is a reaction of the ego to an unconsciously felt, pressing, and at the same time forbidden, impulse (as, for example, when a mother feels a murderous impulse toward a beloved child). Thus, we speak of "instinctual danger," and maintain that there is also some reality in this kind of internal danger—namely, that behind it is a drive which the ego perceives as dangerous and, therefore, must overcome. The difference, then, between reality anxiety and neurotic anxiety is that in the former the danger lies in the external world, while in the latter it lies within the self. What is common to them is that both partake of *reality* danger, since the fulfillment of a forbidden impulse is also dangerous insofar as it threatens the ego's integrity. Thus neurotic anxiety, too, is, in the last analysis, reality anxiety.

There are, however, certain kinds of patients, *actual neurotics* (I prefer to call them *stasis neurotics*), who suffer from anxiety but do not attach their anxiety to any sort of idea, conscious or unconscious. Actual anxiety, or stasis anxiety, is the pure expression of an undischarged need tension, which is converted to anxiety whenever the inner perception of the need or its motor release is unacceptable. The absence of reality danger, then, makes the difference between stasis anxiety and neurotic anxiety; what they do have in common, however, is need tension. We might add that stasis anxiety is without content, while neurotic anxiety is already connected to certain ideas.

A further difficulty in the problem of anxiety is that sometimes anxiety appears as a *result* of instinctual inhibition (stasis anxiety), while at other times it is the very *cause* of the instinctual inhibition. Thus, for example, a little boy's fear of losing his penis is the cause of his repressing the impulse to masturbate. On the other hand, we see that the boy develops anxiety *after* he has repressed his masturbation and may perhaps have developed a fear of the dark as well. How can anxiety as the cause, and anxiety as the result, of instinctual inhibition be reduced to a common denominator? Freud, in "Inhibition, Symptom and Anxiety" (1926), abandoned his original view of anxiety as the result of instinct inhibition and took the position that anxiety is actually the cause of the inhibition.[5] We, on the contrary, do not subscribe to an "either-or" alternative, but see instead a process uniting both views at once. In order to understand this, we must clear up the semantic inaccuracies that arise when we speak of the various kinds of anxiety. The anxiety arising in the masturbating boy because he fears some damage to his penis is not the same as the anxiety affect he develops *after* he has repressed the instinctual drive. The former could very well be a simple fear or expectation of danger, to avoid which he represses his drive. In other words, in the first case, the affect of anxiety does not develop fully but only partially, while in the second case it comes to *full* fruition. In the former case, the emphasis is on *signal anxiety*; in the second, it is on the *affect of anxiety*. Signal anxiety, which leads to repression of the instinctual drive, can only become the affect of anxiety when a need tension (that is, sexual stasis) is already present. This holds true for every sort of anxiety, including reality anxiety.

In homosexuals, for example, we see a "castration anxiety" that keeps them from embracing a woman; but this anxiety becomes an affective experience only if they have been abstinent for a long time. On the other hand, erythrophobes lose their anxiety as soon as they let themselves masturbate—long before the fear of genital injury is resolved.

Thus neurotic anxiety arises from the confluence of objective signal anxiety *and* blocked sexual energy. The defense against the drive (inhibition) leads to stasis and hence the affect of anxiety; on the other hand, the experiencing of anxiety results in the fixation of the instinctual repression.[6]

Just what is the relationship of reality anxiety to stasis anxiety? Is it possible to see these two conditions, so different in their origin, as having a common source? Freud denies this and again differentiates stasis anxiety from other kinds.[7] In a real, acute danger situation, one reacts with anxiety; recalling the episode in fantasy may evoke the original experience of anxiety in proportion to the vividness of the memory. What is so crucial about this? The only answer is—the affect. When vividly recalling a real danger once experienced, the individual reacts as if this danger were once more real. This affect must correspond to a specific bodily innervation which had occurred in the original experience. Stasis anxiety corresponds to a *specific physical innervation*. Is there a common denominator here, or a fundamental difference? The main difference is that, in stasis anxiety, an impulse or instinctual demand, pressing from within toward the outside is not given an opportunity for movement. To cite a comparison: it is as if a compressed gas were kept under pressure and now exerted a counterpressure, which we can equate with the stasis. In the case of reality anxiety, however, especially in panic states, there is a sudden withdrawal of all cathexis to the inside. The end result is the same: an internal blocking of energy. In terms of our analogy, it is as if a gas were first in an uncompressed state and an external force were suddenly to compress it. In both cases, an increase in gas pressure would result; only, in one case, the cause would be a prevention of expansion, while, in the other, it would be compression. Thus reality anxiety and stasis anxiety share a common source, namely dammed-up excitation. Normally, reality anxiety disappears; it does not become fixated. It can, however, continue as neurotic anxiety. This occurs when a realistically experienced danger and its resulting blocked excitation are caught up in an already existing need tension. This is seen most clearly in the traumatic neuroses.

Although we have found that the blocking of excitation is the *common denominator* of every affective anxiety experience (fright, reality anxiety, neurotic anxiety, stasis anxiety), there are still many problems to be solved. How is the excitation of neurotic anxiety related to that of reality anxiety, and how are both related to pure stasis anxiety? Simple consideration leads to the borderland between psyche and soma. The blocking of the excitation is a physiological problem that can be understood from two angles: its subjective psychic and objective somatic expressions.

Sexuality and Anxiety as Antithetical Excitations of the Autonomic Nervous System

In further pursuing the manifestations of anxiety, I was able—as a result of painstaking resistance analysis—to observe directly the change from genital to cardiac excitation, from sexual feeling in the genitals to anxiety sensations in the heart regions.[8]

As long as patients do not allow themselves to become conscious of a sensual sexual excitation, they experience anxiety which is felt as physically localized in the heart and diaphragm regions. If, however, they allow the sexual feelings to become conscious, the anxiety sensation of tension or oppression disappears and the genitals become turgid (erection, vaginal lubrication, etc.) Furthermore, in anxiety, physical symptoms appear that are the exact opposite of those in sexual excitation. Anxiety is characterized by cold shivers (from contraction of the skin blood vessels), pallor, urge to urinate or defecate, sudden sweats, increased heart action, with occasional systolic skipping, and dryness of the mouth; in men, shrinking of the penis; in women, complete dryness of the sex organs (vaginismus). By contrast, sexual excitation shows the following features: feelings of warmth (in women, particularly in the genitals, neck, and breast), turgidity and active secretion by the genital organs, the heart quiet or in diastolic excitation ("cardiac expansion"). In the heart and diaphragm regions there are sensations akin to those of the anxiety state, yet markedly different from them: patients mention "tightness" or "oppression" when they feel anxiety; "expansion" when they feel sexual pleasure. Such expressions are very meaningful to us, for they are the direct language of an inner state of being, as will be shown below.

The antithesis of sexuality and anxiety can easily be shown in other examples. The genitals "shrink" in anxiety (as a result of vasoconstriction) and expand, stretch and fill up in sexual excitation. In fright, there is a sudden energetic emptying of the peripheral blood vessels, especially from the musculature of the extremities, which we experience clearly as a "paralyzed" feeling. If a reflex defense action occurs, the anxiety feeling comes "later"—that is, the sensation of paralysis follows the action; or, after a single strong systole, the heartbeat stops for a few seconds.

Thus, the excitation of the two contrasting states runs its course in the vegetative nervous system, but, in the case of sexual excitation, the *vagal* reaction predominates, while in anxiety the *sympathetic* reaction is uppermost. Here we should note that the vagal and sympathetic, as systems, constitute a functional unity, while possessing at the same time innervations which are antithetical to each other. We also know that, under certain circumstances, both branches of the autonomic nervous system react synchronously—for example, in fright, one may get both peripheral vasoconstriction (sympathetic), as well as a sudden diarrhealike loss of feces and urine; or both branches can simultaneously block each other—for example, blocking of the sympathetic fibers of the celiac ganglion gives rise to hemorrhages of the intestinal mucosa. Furthermore, the feelings of anticipation that occur in both sexual arousal and anxiety states are different and antithetical to each other, yet still related, for in both experiences qualitatively similar sensations occur in the heart and diaphragm regions, the seat of the celiac ganglion. These sensory phenomena must bear a close relationship to the epileptic aura. Careful examination of epileptics reveals that the aura-like sensation preceding the attack has the character of pleasure anxiety, sometimes mainly of pure anxiety, sometimes mainly of pure pleasure; if the latter, it is felt in the genital region.

The above facts justify our modifying the original Freudian assumption that libidinal excitation which is denied motor discharge can "change over" into anxiety. Rather, what is involved is a different kind of innervation and excitation of the vegetative nervous system itself. Thus excitation of the body *periphery* gives rise to sexual sensations, whereas excitation of the body center (heart and diaphragm regions) leads to feelings of anxiety. We thereby formulated for the first time the sex-economic view of the emotions, the concept of a functional antithesis of *body center* and *body periphery*—a concept that has fundamental significance.

Our view that pleasure (sexual excitation) and anxiety are antithetical phenomena within the same nervous apparatus, that is, the vegetative apparatus, ties in with the view well known in the physiology of anxiety—namely, that there is a functional relationship between anxiety and vegetative excitation. The *new* factor we introduce is that, first of all, the vegetative system also has a relationship to the sexual function (as the antithesis of the anxiety function) and that here, too, an *antithetical* innervation of the vegetative apparatus is involved. On the basis of the above, let us now proceed to present evidence that the system, Sexuality-Vegetative Apparatus-Anxiety, is functionally identical to the system of fluid movement (blood and cellular fluid) of the organism.

The Misch Choline Experiment

The physiological problem of anxiety has been approached from many angles. The tie-in with carbon dioxide regulation in tachycardia, the anxiety attacks accompanying angina pectoris, the spasms of bronchial asthma, and similar illnesses pointed constantly to a definite physiological factor in anxiety. Painstaking research into the function of the orgasm had started with the problem of anxiety as a complex psychic phenomenon and had probed it to the boundary of the physiological realm. It remained for the latter to provide the rest of the solution, like the apposition of two sides of a tunnel. However, this did not occur, partly because nerve physiology was stuck in mechanistic neuromuscular experimentation that allowed of no theoretical meeting ground; also, because the connection between anxiety and sexuality, the key to the problem, was frowned upon in physiology, and the door was blocked by traditional attitudes toward sexuality, long since proven wrong. It was all the more significant, then, that two analytically trained psychiatrists, Doctors Walter and Käthe Misch, attempted to approach the physiology of anxiety by means of pharmacological experiments, and they did this by taking the problem of anxiety neurosis as their starting point.

They were very skillful in combining the therapeutic with the theoretical. Their article on "The Vegetative Origin of Neurotic Anxiety and Its Medical Treatment" (*Der Nervenzarzt*, Vol. 5, No. 8, 1932), notes that in their lengthy reports at the 1910 Congress, Oppenheim and Hoche had pointed out the futility of all medical efforts of a pharmacological or hydro-therapeutic nature.

The Misch experiments started out with the pure syndrome of anxiety neurosis (peripheral vasoconstriction, tachycardia, arterial hypotonia, mydriasis, decreased salivary secretion, cold sweats, debility of the musculature, with tremor and diarrhea), symptoms which point to a high degree of autonomic excitation, predominantly sympathetic. It was easy to assume that there must be a drug that would remove the anxiety syndrome, dilate the peripheral blood vessels, slow down the heart, lower the blood pressure, promote salivary secretion, and restore the striated musculature—in other words, an agent that would affect the parasympathetic system. The whole group of choline preparations turned out to be just such agents, which, in the authors' words, "fit into the somatic anxiety syndrome like a key into its lock"; these can "not only do away with the somatic anxiety syndrome, but can also put an end to the psychic experience of anxiety in a flash." Intramuscular administration of 0.1 percent acetylcholine produced within a few minutes marked erythema, a subsidence of the tachycardia almost to normal, and the disappearance of subjective physical symptoms. At the same time, the anxiety state, usually so intractable, vanished, giving way to a feeling of complete well-being. When choline preparations were given orally (Pacyl, four to six tablets [daily]; Hypotan, three tablets daily) there was no recurrence of severe anxiety states.

It was further shown that the effect of choline is greater the more free-floating and unanchored the anxiety. (In cases of compulsion neuroses, for example, not much could be accomplished.) They attributed the results mainly to the counteracting effect of the choline on the sympathetic nervous system. Table 1 depicts the two syndromes, according to Misch.

Table 1

	Anxiety Syndrome	Choline Effect
Peripheral blood vessels of the skin	contract	dilate
Heart action	speeds up	slows down
Blood pressure	rises	falls
Pupils	dilate	constrict
Salivary secretion	diminishes	increases
Musculature	loses normal tone	regains normal tone

In contrast to the authors of this excellent experiment, I prefer to emphasize the theoretical rather than the practical, therapeutic aspects, since prevention of anxiety seems more important to me than its treatment, though I do not in any way minimize the latter. But the far-reaching question of preventing neurosis demands, first of all, the most complete theoretical application of this experiment. I had already postulated, from my psychoanalytic treatment of the neuroses, that the problem of the "somatic core of the neurosis" is a pathological state of excitation of the vegetative nervous system. This experiment does so much to confirm this view that it seems worthwhile to pursue it further.

The Two Primordial Forms of Psychic Tendencies: "Toward the World"—"Away from the World"

If we now pursue the antithesis of sexual excitation and anxiety in its psychic ramifications—if we look for its expressions in so-called "higher" psychic functions—we strike, first of all, a mass of seemingly unrelated mechanisms and functions. To begin with, if we classify them genetically and theoretically, the assumption of a basic antithesis in autonomic life functions is unavoidable for an understanding of the higher psychic antitheses. Psychoanalysis differentiates a whole series of psychic pairs of antithetical strivings, beginning with the *individual* versus the *external world*. The libidinal interest directed toward the self is called *narcissistic libido*; that which is directed toward the external world, *object libido*. The latter arises from the "narcissistic reservoir" of libidinal energy. The cathexis of objects of the external world is likened to the ameba's sending out pseudopods, which can then be retracted. This "pulling-in of the libido," the withdrawal of interest, is considered a return to the "narcissistic" state, as, for example, in falling asleep; yet, at any time, the interest can be directed outward from the ego toward objects (as in waking up, falling in love, etc.). Object libido can again become narcissistic libido, since its origin is in the narcissistic libido. The opposition between the individual and the external world is accordingly represented as a conflict between narcissistic libido and object libido. While both kinds of libido constitute a single entity, they can also come into opposition with one another. This occurs when object gratification comes into conflict with the narcissistic need for self-preservation. The incestuous love of a little boy for his mother regularly conflicts with his narcissistic self-interest, especially in terms of his concern for his penis. Thus renunciation of a drive and repression of an object-directed impulse regularly stem from narcissistic interests and result, first, in a withdrawal of object cathexis.

Let us examine another antithetical pair—namely, an aggressive impulse and the anxiety aroused at the prospect of discharging the aggression. We would immediately see this anxiety as arising *solely* from the blocked impulse since every aggressive impulse that is blocked results in anxiety. The only question is whether the aggression is a primary drive (as more recent analytic theory maintains) or a secondary drive, which I believe it must be. The psychoanalysis of ambivalence teaches us that aggression is a reaction to the denial of libidinal gratification. Aggression and libidinal striving have in common that both reach out *toward the world* or toward objects in the world; they are differentiated only by their aim. The libidinal drive seeks to achieve pleasure; the destructive drive seeks to abolish a source of unpleasure in the external world, either by destroying the object of unpleasure or by incorporating it. Libido and aggression thus have the same tendency—toward the world; however, in their goals, they show a decided antithesis. If, simultaneously, one loves and hates the *same* object, the love impulse tends to put a brake on the hate impulse and to transform it into a guilt feeling, as a compromise between love and hate directed toward the *same* object. On the other hand, frustrated love can turn into hate or can enormously increase existing hate. From the mixture of sexuality and destructiveness, sadism arises. Perhaps the best way to express this phenomenon is to say: if the individual cannot get to the world by way of love, then he will try to destroy it. Put in another way, the individual will replace the unattained libidinal gratification with an act of agression. The common antithesis to both types of object striving is anxiety, which I see essentially as a *flight away from the world* into the self. This is what we mean by narcissistic regression—that is, the withdrawal of cathexis into the self. It may come about through an external blocking of drive gratification or by an internal prohibition against approaching the outside world. In both cases, anxiety, or incipient anxiety, ensues. The tendency *"toward the world"* (libidinal or aggressive) is thus basically opposed to the tendency *"away from the world."* The latter, in its most primitive biological state, is seen as a withdrawal into the self; on a higher biological plane, this reaction is never lost; it is only supplemented by a secondary muscular one, [namely], spatial separation from the primary source of the unpleasure. In the further development of coping with the external world, there appears the aggressive removal of the source of the unpleasure or danger (destruction) and, finally, intellectual foresight and mastery of external difficulties.

From these functional relationships, we can deduce that destructive aggression, which plays such a major role in social as well as individual life, represents a phylogenetically and an ontogenetically later function than the two primary drives, sexuality and anxiety. It will be shown that this slight difference from Freud's view that libido and aggression are drives stemming from the same biological level, has far-reaching clinical and theoretical as well as sociological differences. Thus, sex economy denies the primary character of destructive drives and sees them, rather, as deriving phylogenetically from the function of dammed-up libido on the one hand, and from avoidance of anxiety on the other. The fact that the muscular system, the apparatus of destruction, has its origin in the mesoderm, that is, a secondary embryonic structure, while the apparatus of the sexual and anxiety functions is already present in the protozoon, may strengthen this view from the standpoint of historical development.

The following considerations are crucial to an understanding of the psychic apparatus: the blocking of either an aggressive or libidinal drive produces anxiety, but anxiety is avoided whenever the aggression is blocked or turned against the self —in other words, when it has become a self-destructive trend. Elsewhere I attempted to explain in detail why I have to reject the assumption of a primary drive toward self-destruction, and why I see all phenomena pertaining to it in a different light. In any event, the development of anxiety stands in an antithetical relationship to masochistic, self-destructive tendencies—which contradicts the view of many analysts that anxiety is the expression of an inner perception of self-destructive tendencies. The latter holds true only if we differentiate blocked aggression from aggression against the self.

Let us summarize our genetic view of the pairs of contrasting drives:

Genetic-Dialectic Antithesis of Drives

External World	Ego
Object libido	Narcissistic libido
Object cathexis	Anxiety
Libidinal object cathexis	Aggression (combination results in sadism)
Aggression	Anxiety
Aggression	Self-destruction through turning against the self (masochism)
Drive	Morality

Steps in the Development of the Anxiety Reaction

Narcissistic regression (withdrawal into the self; protozoic reaction)

Flight (spatial removal from the object; metazoic reaction)

Destruction (abolition of the source of danger; metazoic reaction)

Civilized coping with existence (intellectual planning; human-social reaction)

Object Relation ("Toward the World")	Narcissistic Relation ("Away from the World")
Object love	(Sexual) anxiety
Hate-object introjection	(Aggressive) anxiety
Object destruction	Guilt feeling or self-destruction
Coping with tasks (work accomplishment)	Schizophrenic autism

So much for the psychological postulates derived from the reduction of complex phenomena to simple ones. They support our main point concerning anxiety neurosis, namely, the antithesis of sexual excitation and anxiety. Neither hate (destruction or aggression) nor drives toward self-destruction, neither muscular flight nor intellectual mastery of dangers, are met with in pure anxiety neurosis. The latter seems to us particularly suitable for discussing the problem of the border line between the psyche and soma.

The psychoanalytic theory of drives understood the antithetical nature of the drives, but differed from the dialectic approach in its lack of genetic derivation of this antithesis and in the assumption of an *absolute* basic dualism of the drives (Eros-death instinct). It made its major contribution when it tried to understand the organic in terms of drive dynamics, but was forced to land in the metaphysics of the death instinct, because it provided the inorganic with a soul [psyche], without directly deriving the source of the psyche itself from the inorganic. And it lost the chance of finding a way out of the metaphysical blind alley, when its proponents viewed our attempts at a dialectical-materialistic solution as a hostile act against the very heart of the theory. In doing so, the psychoanalytic theory of drives had become subservient to its religious and social milieu and had thereby sacrificed its scientific future.

Tendency to Assume Spherical Shape

Approaching the problem from a different angle, it is easy to show that many living organisms in a state of flight from the world, that is, in *narcissistic* regression, have a tendency to assume a spherical shape; or, when there is a fully developed skeleton, approximate that shape. A few examples will suffice.

If one touches the horns of a snail with a blade of grass, the snail retracts its horns but otherwise remains motionless. After a while, it will slowly extend its horns. When touched again, it retracts its horns more quickly than it did before and also starts withdrawing into its shell.

An earthworm at rest or in motion is elongated, "loose." If touched on the head, it will pull back, becoming shorter and fatter, or else it will curl up. Where the capacity to withdraw into itself has been lost, we no longer see a change from elongated to spherical shape, but, rather, a *curling up of the body* —in other words, a sort of illusory spherical form. That is what happens when a hedgehog is threatened. The extremities are drawn up close to the body, the back is rounded, and the head is drawn close to the legs. One thinks of the position of the embryo, which, of course, is not an "anxiety position" but represents an adaptation to the smallest space.

In the protozoon, one can best observe this drawing back into the self. The pseudopodia, which earlier had given the cell a multiform appearance, disappear; surface irregularities are smoothed out; the cell assumes an increasingly ball-like shape. Similarly, before cell division and after copulation, the spherical form predominates.

The "shaking with fright" of the metazoon is doubtless similar in principle. The teleological explanation—that a smaller area offers less surface to be attacked—does not suffice. This superficial, rationalistic interpretation only brings us closer to theology, but not a step further. We can explain this phenomenon differently.

If a cat feels threatened, its first movement is to hunch its back, that is, its vertebral column. The contraction of the piloerector muscles likewise belongs here; this appears as "hair standing on end." The spherical shape, either in the form of withdrawal of protruding organs (pseudopods, snail's horns, etc.) or of curving of the back and retraction of head and extremities, thus appears as a result of the tendency "away from the world." In contrast, we see bodily elongation, extension of the extremities and head, in short, a "spreading outward from the body's center" as a result of the function "toward the world." Later we will recognize the logical extension of this function in the fusion of two organisms.

But first, we must examine a few facts which reveal the above-mentioned functions in their basic vegetative form.

3. The Antithesis of Sexuality and Anxiety: The Basic Autonomic Model

Fluid Flow and Psychic "Trend" in the Organism

To understand what follows, let us summarize matters up to this point:

1. In anxiety states, the body fluids, blood and other liquids, flow away from the periphery. In sexual excitation we find the opposite: heightened turgor of peripheral blood vessels; erythema of skin and mucous membranes; increased secretion of salivary and genital glands.

2. Sudden chemotaxic dilatation of the peripheral vessels relieves anxiety (choline effect). Blocking of sexual motility.

that is, of peripheral turgor, produces anxiety (adrenalin effect).

3. On a phenomenological basis—quite apart from these physiological findings—we are compelled to postulate in the psychic apparatus two directions of psychic interest: "toward the world" and its opposite, "away from the world."

4. In the biological world, quite generally we find two antithetical directions or functions, resulting in the spherical form or its opposite, elongation and expansion.

We note that everywhere the direction of fluid flow is the same as the psychic direction, or, better, the biological direction. The tendency "toward the world," expansion, corresponds to the centrifugal flow, the tendency "away from the world," assumption of the spherical form, and anxiety formation corresponds to the centripetal flow. We especially want to know whether we are dealing with a coincidental similarity, or an important, hitherto overlooked *fundamental* law of living things. It would be of the utmost significance for our concept of the functional identity of psychic and somatic functions. Let us, then, bring together a few elementary facts, the sum total of which will enable us to understand clearly a series of otherwise totally incomprehensible relationships between psychic and somatic functions.

In unicellular organisms, as well as in multicellular life forms that have not yet evolved a circulatory system, we note a plasma movement that bears a certain orderly relationship to primitive life functions. In plant cells, the plasma shows rotating and circulatory movements. These movements respond promptly to electrical stimulation. Thus weak electrical stimuli slow down the plasma movements, while strong stimuli stop them completely.

The nature of plasma movement, whether spontaneous or altered by electrical stimuli, is seen most clearly in the amoeba. Its protoplasm contains corpuscular elements that turn out to be round, water-filled vesicles. The so-called contractile vacuole is such a spherical vesicle, which, from time to time, breaks down and discharges its fluid content. According to Max Hartmann, the movement of the amoeba is directly related to the plasma flow. When the amoeba moves forward, plasma flows from the center to the periphery, and thus the plasma pseudopod first comes into being. It is then retracted into the amoeba's body. If the amoeba is touched, the plasma flow is reversed—that is, the plasma flows from the periphery of the pseudopod back into the center. The withdrawal of the pseudopod corresponds to this. If the amoeba has put out several pseudopods and by chance touches something solid, the plasma flows in the direction of the pseudopod contacting the solid, while the other pseudopods are withdrawn by the emptying of the plasma.

When the amoeba is ingesting food, the plasma always flows toward the periphery. The amoeba reacts negatively to chemical, thermal, electric, and photic stimui—that is, the plasma flow is deflected from the latter. According to Rhumbler, Engelmann, Harrington, Davenport, and others, if light is suddenly thrown on food being ingested by an amoeba, the creature stops feeding, even disgorges the devoured shreds, and draws into itself. An amoeba flows freely in red light, is stopped by blue light, but always moves in the direction of continuous beams of light. In the amoeba there is nothing but the vegetative plasma flow to sustain the system of life processes.

Let us summarize the most important biological discoveries regarding plasma flow and the structuring of forms that accompanies it. First, according to Rhumbler, during centrifugal plasma flow, the cell body's thin, fluid plasma mass (endoplasm) is changed into the thick, fluid plasma of the periphery (ectoplasm). During centripetal flow (also called spherogenic flow), when the flow is in the opposite direction, the thick, fluid ectoplasm is changed into thin, fluid endoplasm. This observation may well confirm Kraus's idea that what we are seeing here, in the basic living phenomenon of movement, is hydration or dehydration of a colloidal substance—in other words, a change in the density of the substance through *change in the water content*.

According to Max Hartmann, most phenomena pertaining to the movement of pseudopods show that the physical state of the protoplasm is primarily fluid. The movement itself, according to available studies, is a result of the continuous change from expansion to contraction, in the plasma of one-celled organisms no less than in the muscles of multicellular ones. Here, too, there is a change from *contraction* (tendency: spherical form) to *expansion* (tendency: elongated form). In another connection, we shall return to fluid movement as the common denominator of plasma movement and muscle movement. Significantly, according to Hofer and Gruber, protoplasmic bodies that have lost their nuclei will go on forming pseudopods for days on end.

Everyone agrees with the well-known view of Bütschli, Berthold, and Quincke, that the flowing movement of pseudopods can be explained by hydromechanical laws of surface tension. At the boundary between two immiscible fluids (as, for example, oil and water, or salt electrolyte and colloid electrolyte), surface tension and surface energies come into play, as they do in plasma also. There are two aspects to these energies: first, the internal pressure exerted from the center outward, which seeks to enlarge the surface; second, the surface tension exerted from the periphery to the center (and, beyond this, tangentially toward the surface curvature). The internal pressure is in direct proportion to the surface tension and in inverse proportion to the radius. If the surface tension of the surrounding medium is lower than that of a drop of plasma, the plasma surface tension wins out and a spherical form perforce results (state of equilibrium). It is thought that a pseudopod is formed when, for any reason, the surface tension falls at any spot on the surface. This idea misses the essence of the process, for, in that case, there would be only *passive* movement. Actually, the plasma flow arising from within points to an *active* process from the inside. This might perhaps lead to too hasty vitalistic assumptions, which we have every reason to avoid. Certainly, the effect of the internal pressure alone does not suffice to explain the endogenous tendency toward expansion, for then we would have to know why the nonliving drop is *not* in motion though it, too, has a pressure from within. In the living organism, however, there must be something other than mechanical tension to produce active motion.

Of importance in this connection are Bütschli's experimental models set up to demonstrate the plasma flow in living organisms. When water drops are left standing with a mixture of oil drops and calcium carbonate over a period of time, oil foam drops result which, after a rinse with water, usually begin to flow without much change in shape. If the water is replaced by thinned-out glycerine and the oil drops pressed down by a glass slide, they not only float about but form variously shaped continua. In addition, one can observe the same *centrifugal* axial streams and counterstreams at the edges that are seen in the amoeba in a state of pseudopod formation. And, in amoeba and oil drop alike, a temperature elevation greatly speeds up the formation of artificial pseudopods.

Hartmann considers surface energy to be the prime mover in pseudopod formation but thinks that, despite the many hypotheses, no one has explained what causes a rise or fall in surface tension. According to Jensen, anabolism is supposed to cause decreased surface tension, while catabolism results in an increase—accordingly, in the former, there is an expansion; in the latter, a contraction. The essence of this process is supposed to be an increase in the number of molecules in catabolism or a corresponding decrease in anabolism.

Be that as it may, we still have no reason to doubt that in the two opposing directions of the amoeba's plasma flow, the archetype is laid down for the two psychic directions postulated above: the "sexual" toward the world and the "anxious" away from the world. Here some corollary problems arise, which, with one exception, we shall merely touch upon but not pursue further in this paper.

First, it is clear that the leap from passive motion, caused by mechanical change in the oil drop's surface tension, to the active, *endogenously* conditioned plasma flow of the amoeba, holds within itself the riddle of the origin of the living from the nonliving.

In addition, the problem of surface tension leads us to the question of cell division, which we will discuss elsewhere.

Finally, the question arises as to how we go from the two directions of plasma flow to the complicated libido-anxiety phenomenon. For only by demonstrating continuity of function can we establish our basic hypothesis that sexuality and anxiety are antithetical primary functions of living matter.

Kraus's "Fluid Theory of Life"

After I rejected the primary dualism of sexuality and death instinct postulated [by psychoanalysis],[9] the logical continuation of psychoanalytic libido theory led toward a basic concept—that is, in addition to the frequently described relationship between fluid flow and anxiety or sexual excitation, there is a functional antithesis between the *center of the organism* and the *periphery*. We begin to understand anxiety, fundamentally, as a *central* stasis of fluid (psychologically expressed as a central "excitation"); and pleasure, in general, as well as sexual pleasure in particular, as a peripheral expansion of the bodily fluid (psychologically, a peripheral excitation). In the former case [anxiety], there is simultaneously a peripheral discharge of fluid and a *central* excitation. In the latter [pleasure], a central discharge and *peripheral* excitation. In the anxiety state, tension is felt centrally (congestion); in sexual tension it is felt peripherally (as in erection). The question remains whether these tension states have any connection with decrease in surface tension in peripheral discharge or the increase in surface tension in peripheral hyperemia. To clarify this, let us recall the actions of two drugs, adrenalin and alcohol, which have opposite effects on the circulatory system. The physiologic effect of adrenalin is the direct production of anxiety. Alcohol reduces tension and anxiety, as does choline, through dilatation of the peripheral vessels. We then must know more thoroughly the relationship of the vegetative apparatus to the vascular apparatus, since it stands in concrete, functional relationship to the affect of anxiety as well as to sexual excitation.

Let us turn now to Kraus's "fluid theory of life" [*Nässe Theorie des Lebens*]. In my estimation, it seems to do the job expected of a nerve physiology text, that is, to summarize the phenomena and functions of living substance in a basic, unified view. I would minimize the objection that it would be dangerous to build on this theory because it is, itself, controversial, since there are certain criteria for the usefulness and correctness of a theory that make a judgment possible. From psychoanalysis, we know how seldom new discoveries can count on the favorable response of colleagues in particular and scientists in general. There is not too much to be said for the oft-extolled objectivity of scientific criticism. Living in the midst of the scientific hustle and bustle shows us how greatly criticism is beclouded by personal likes and dislikes, traditional thinking, and friendships within the specialty field. It is almost impossible to make an objective judgment on new theories in a specialty with which one is unfamiliar. To rely only on the plausibility of a new viewpoint seems dangerous, because the plausible need not always be right and, also, because there is too much risk of lapsing into preconceived notions and biases. When, however, several disciplines, *independently* and without any inkling of their respective results, or any preconceived idea of agreeing with one another, always seem to converge toward one certain conclusion and toward similar or identical views; when, finally, certain problems can be solved only by such two or three independently arrived-at theories and not by any others—then we have no doubt that *these* theories, and not heuristically valueless, isolated ones, have the greater probability of being right.

By the same token, when it is shown that certain discoveries of the biologist Hartmann, the internist Kraus, and the psychologist Freud, arrived at independently, all converge in a certain direction; when, finally, my own sex-economic research into the function of the orgasm and its relationship to the vegetative nervous system leads me in the same direction; when the above-cited findings partly confirm my theories and partly serve to form a unified picture of the psyche-soma relationship—then we cannot allow doubts about a strange new theory to deter us from using it, so long as the critics do not have a better, more plausible one to take its place.

I will limit my presentation of Kraus's theory to the basic points essential to an understanding of our problem. For the reader who wishes to delve more deeply, I recommend a careful study of Kraus's work "Allegemeine und spezielle Pathologie der Person" (*Klinische Syzygiologie,* Leipzig: Theime, 1926).

First, let us recall that in the plasma movement of the amoeba we determined in principle the same two antithetical directions seen in the tendency "toward the world" and "away from the world"; and that, further, the psychic tendencies and the physiological direction of the fluids are in the closest conceivable relationship to each other.

Some of Kraus's basic ideas concretely approximate my own views derived from character analysis.

Kraus starts from the premise that living substance is essentially composed of colloids. Colloids are solutions of substances in water that do not show molecular dissolution, but rather flocculation into quite large particles. From colloid solution to salt solution there are many gradations. Thus, the distinct boundary between the organic and inorganic, so long controversial, becomes blurred. The colloid, like the salt solution, is an electrolyte; it is differentiated from the salt solution by its inability to permeate a membrane. Kraus sees in the biosystem an arousal system, a "relaylike" release mechanism, an apparatus for charging (that is, storing) and discharging energy—located throughout on the energetically charged boundary surfaces. The most important boundary surfaces are those located between salt electrolyte and colloid electrolyte. The life process is characterized by the ability to remove oxygen, the production of carbon dioxide, and the generation of electrical energy at the boundary surfaces. Salt solution is an essential factor for life, appearing long before the development of blood. To Kraus, the transport and distribution of substances appear to be far more important for the reproduction of life processes than metabolism, that is, than the purely chemical transformation of the ingested substances themselves.

The life process may be defined as a *self-activating* vegetative flow, essentially as *fluid convection*. We must differentiate the following: the mechanical convection of fluid, such as blood and lymph circulation; the directed convection of digestive juices; and, finally, most important of all, the microscopic movement of protoplasm. The overall movement of fluids in the organism has far more significance than merely that of supplying various regions with nutritive substances; rather, functioning occurs only because border surfaces of varying potential are formed, in endless number, between fluids of different densities and composition. To these charged boundary surfaces, the purely mechanical surface tensions are added as a vectoral factor. *The biosystem functions through equalization of boundary surface tensions*—that is, the surfaces of unequal charge behave exactly like electrodes in an electrolytic system. The organic membranes and interfaces between the salt electrolyte and colloid electrolyte function mainly as boundary surfaces. In order for an electric current to flow, there must be not only a charging of the membranes (electrodes), but also a connection between the two; the body fluids, being electrolytes, serve as this connection, but not only as that. The biosystem itself not only generates electrical energy, but also equalizes these charges and generates currents between and within the inner membranes through the conducting substance of the organism itself. Thus a conductor experimentally placed from without would only result in a short circuit. The electricity arises from the movement of fluids; in the capillaries, for example, according to Kraus, unbound electrical charges wander about freely. The potential gradients mentioned originate in the boundary surface between fluid in motion and fluid at rest. In their equalization, electrical energy is converted into mechanical energy.

However, this "fluid theory of life" is validated only when what occurs in the protoplasm can be brought into some sort of relationship with the laws of colloidal solutions.

Let us consider briefly this theory of Kraus. He is undoubtedly describing, without labeling it, the same process I regard as the basis of the orgasm—that is, transformation of mechanical tension into electrical charge (*tension-charge process*); then, transformation of electrical discharge back into mechanical discharge (*discharge-release process*). Accordingly, the orgasm would be the most potent special case of general vegetative movement.

If, in the mimosa plant, one touches the lower half of the pulvinus, or perhaps applies a heat stimulus, the leaf falls—there is negative galvanization. At the same time, one observes a discharge of water from the leaf joint and a corresponding decrease in turgor. If, on the other hand, one stimulates the upper side, the leaf elongates. If the mechanical reaction is blocked, the electrical one still occurs. If, when the twig is immersed in water, the pulvinus becomes overly turgid, that is, erect, the leaf does not drop, because it is difficult to expel the water. All plants and plant organs react electrically.

Thus we maintain that water absorption goes hand in hand with an increase in turgor and expansion ("erection"); water expulsion, with the leaf's falling and a decrease in turgor. The significance of this experiment for an understanding of penile tumescence and detumescence will be shown elsewhere. In principle, the processes are functionally identical.

In the tiny cells of Cucurbita pepo, which has a circular plasma movement, Velten found a plasma combination consisting of a darker, more colloidal substance and a lighter, more watery, hyaline substance. Both together, according to Kraus, form the so-called critical fluid mixture, which is a basic characteristic of all living substances. On observing microscopically the behavior of such "critical fluid mixtures" in living substances, we see that the granules are initially at rest. If granules from the denser layer reach the thinner, less viscous layer, those with a greater water content show lively Brownian movement. If a weak induction current is now sent through the cell, a great number of granules begin to show molecular movement; the flow slows down. When the electrical effect gets stronger, swellings appear at various points. Then the plasma cord either shows spherical excrescences or sends out fine plasma threads. If the stimulus is interrupted, the excrescences are again withdrawn, and the regular plasma flow continues. The swellings are accounted for by absorption of water from the layer of plasma with the greater water content. This can continue until the swelling site is completely severed from the plasma cord and swims about freely in the cellular fluid.

Every organic body shows a stable hydrodynamic system, the most essential functions of which are metabolism for tissue growth and for eliminating solids, metabolic wastes, and salts; water evaporation from the heart and lungs; water replenishment through ingestion of food and drink and from metabolism, etc. The water content of bodies remains the same, on the average. According to Kraus, in adults it is approximately 70 percent; blood is 80 percent, skin 70 percent, the brain 75 percent, and so on. We have already indicated that the plasma movement is most important. Stern[10] was able to determine that the plasma movement is slowed down by weak electrical stimuli and stopped by stronger ones. Essentially, the following changes occur in plasma when stimuli are applied: intermittent acceleration and deceleration, tumescence and detumescence, expansion and contraction, mixing and separating, precipitation and dissolving of substances, appearance and disappearance of granules; also, changes in viscosity (Kraus).

The effects of stimuli (electrical as well as others) consist of rearrangements of ions and changes in ion concentration in medium, cell fluid, and plasma.

A. W. Greeley was the first to test the general idea that the effects of an electrical current on ions are due to changes in ion concentration and their effect on the colloidal system. He found that acids and salts with cations of higher valence make the plasma more viscous, while alkalis and salts with anions of higer valence make it more fluid. From this, Kraus reached a basic conclusion: if every stimulus applied to a protoplasmic substance threatens the stability of the colloidal substance, it is because the complexes of colloid-inorganic electrolytes become rearranged; this generates changes in the energy potentials at the membrane surfaces, which in turn promotes electrical discharge. Now, since organisms are constantly exposed to external and internal stimuli, it follows that the basic characteristic of living matter is the change in energy potential and the equalization of potential gradients that occur as an alternation between charge and discharge, tension and relaxation.

At this point, we may raise a basic question. Charge and discharge, tension and relaxation, are physical processes which govern inorganic nature as well. To begin with, that which is living is differentiated from the inorganic by a *self-activating* alternation of these functions. What produces this self-activation? The investigation of the function of the orgasm, in which we see a fundamental process of living matter, taught us that tension and charge, discharge and relaxation, stand in a certain functional relationship to each other. Mechanical tension leads to an electrical charge, and the electrical discharge leads to a mechanical relaxation, which, in turn, is transformed into mechanical tension, and so on. Is it, perhaps, just this specific relationship of mechanics and electricity that constitutes the essential characteristic of living matter? We will return frequently to this question.

It is important for our study to consider, first, that analytic psychology sees the basic mechanism of the psychic apparatus as a system of alternating "libidinal" tensions and relaxations, so to speak. Our concept of drives stands or falls on the idea that we are dealing with psychic events, tension and relaxation, charge and discharge of energy. That would have less meaning if it were merely an analogy. But there is more to it than that: there are homologies; there are identities.

We cannot give here, in full, the comprehensive and enlightening arguments that Kraus has provided to clarify his thought processes for the reader. Neither is it important in this connection to submit his arguments to criticism. We would not be in any position to furnish such criticism. Assuming the correctness of his basic concept, that the living system (consisting of the organic boundary surfaces, the colloid electrolyte/salt electrolyte system, the biosystem as the electrolytic relay apparatus, etc.) is activated by the vegetative fluid flow, then Kraus's experiments on living preparations take on an extraordinary importance for us. We shall briefly summarize them. Their point of departure is a view which Kraus has summarized as follows: "There is no individual life process which cannot in some way, directly or indirectly, completely or partially, be explained by ion activity. Like oxygen, electrolytes cannot be replaced by anything else. Most illnesses, too, functional as well as so-called organic ones, have their ultimate basis in the vegetative flow."

Potassium and Calcium as Vegetatively Functioning Ions

The animal organism coordinates a voluntary muscle innervation with an involuntary innervation (independent of consciousness) of smooth muscles, glands, and circulatory system, for the performance of vegetative functions (of heart, intestines, and sexual organs). However, vegetative function is contained in the voluntary muscles, perhaps in the form of muscle tone, as the result of continuous vegetative innervation. In the celebrate, the vegetative system is represented by a particular type of nervous organization, that is, the joining together of sympathetic and parasympathetic ganglia. We may ask if living organisms without a developed vegetative apparatus have something which performs those tasks later evolved as vegetative system functions: peristalsis, circulation, muscle tone, and turgor. In metazoa lacking a skeletal system, we already find nerve ganglia developed. In unicellular and multicellular organisms, up to a certain stage of development, there is no regularly structured nervous system. What, then, takes the place of that function in such creatures? This raises a question as to the morphological forerunner of the vegetative nervous apparatus. Such completely unspeculative questions are necessary when we start from unconscious psychic processes and arrive at problems of living function in general.

For a long time, physiology has studied the specific effect of ions upon the colloidal system, the basic substance of all living matter. If there are chemical substances

first, that can *strengthen* or *weaken* the effects of vegetative innervation;

second, that can *replace* these effects;

third, that can *potentiate* or *neutralize* each other in their effect; and, finally,

fourth, that are a specific component of protoplasm, as, for
     example, lecithin-cholesterol—
then one is justified in assuming that these inorganic substances,
prior to the development of the vegetative apparatus, fulfill
its later functions. It is even possible that this apparatus is
an organized, later development of simple chemical substances.

Here the experimental attempts of Kraus, Zondek, and Dressel, among others, when basically in accord, are of pioneer
significance.

Kraus concludes from his experiments that, in the biological
system, the effect of nerves, drugs, and electrolytes are mutually interchangeable with respect to tissue hydration or dehydration (which, as we learned, is the basic function of living
matter). Organic tissues are a combination of membranes and
fluids. The membranes are complexes of protein, phosphates,
and sterols; they also contain colloids, especially lecithin and
cholesterol. Salt electrolytes are found in the most diverse
forms and combinations. Only those salts in dissolved, ionized
form are chemically active as stimulants—especially the cations
(sodium, potassium, calcium, magnesium, and iron), and the
anions (chloride, phosphate, sulfate, iodide, and carbon dioxide). These salt electrolytes either slow down or speed up
the water flow, especially tissue hydration and dehydration.
Since tumescence and detumescence are directly related to
variations in surface tension, they are basic to the biophysical
problem of tension and discharge. "In the interaction between
colloid electrolytes and certain antagonistic salt electrolytes
for the hydration of colloid membranes and particles lies all
functioning and all functional adaptation."

Zondek began by pointing out that potassium (as well as
sodium) has a diastolic, that is, relaxing effect, which leads
to peripheral expansion; while calcium, on the contrary, has
a systolic or constricting effect, giving rise to central tension.
What we are concerned with, essentially, is the movement
of fluids: one ion brings water to the heart, another removes
water. Kraus and Zondek directly observed the water flow
in a frog preparation and were also able to divert it away from
the curve of the main flow. In other experiments, it was found
that *the vagus acts like an addition of potassium* to the nutrient
fluid of a muscle preparation, *the sympathetic like an addition
of calcium.*

Kraus comes to the perfectly logical conclusion that nerves and muscles are not independent structures, but, rather, that the nervous and muscular systems together form a "syzygy" or functional unity. In particular, "... the vegetative nervous system, in its role as a protoplasm connector, sets up relationships between the membranes of different organs." As a connective plasma mass, the nervous system is subject to the laws of colloid electrolytes. Thus the potassium and calcium groups, with their antithetical effects, are always present. The vegetative nervous system is merely continuing, in an organized way, a function which, in principle, already exists in animals lacking a nervous system, namely: the function of plasma flow, hydration and dehydration, contraction and expansion, tension and discharge, by means of the ions of the salt electrolyte. We must now establish that cholesterol and lecithin, components never missing from organic colloids, behave in the same way as calcium and the sympathetic system, or potassium and the parasympathetic. The antithesis between lecithin and cholesterol is first expressed by the fact that lecithin is a hydrophilic, that is, water-absorbing, colloid, while cholesterol is a hydrophobic, or water-repelling, colloid. Dressel set up a lecithin-cholesterol mixture as a physiological model in order to test the effects of salt electrolyte on colloidal substances. Under certain conditions, (approaching a physiological concentration similar to the electrolyte's molecular structure), the following occurs: when a lecithin-cholesterol mixture is added to potassium or calcium chloride, the antagonism between the ions becomes evident. Thus potassium chloride causes an increase in surface tension of the lecithin-cholesterol mixture, while calcium chloride causes a decrease. Alkali behaves like calcium, acid like potassium. This is highly important to our understanding of certain organ-neurotic phenomena.

A lecithin-Ringer solution applied to a frog's heart stops the heart in *diastole*, that is, it has a *vagal* effect, while the cholesterol-Ringer solution does the same in *systole*, producing a *sympathetic* effect. *However, this effect on the heart muscle is antithetical to the effect on the peripheral muscle*. Potassium causes a tonic contraction of the peripheral muscle, or potentiates the effect of an electrical stimulus. Calcium, on the other hand, diminishes the effect of an electrical stimulus and causes the muscle to relax. This antithetical effect of the electrolytes on heart and peripheral muscle, which Kraus does not further explain, is of great significance to our investigation. It clearly indicates the antithesis of effects between central heart function and peripheral muscular organ function. In this antithesis, also, calcium and potassium behave exactly like the sympathetic and the vagus. Vagal innervation enhances the tone of the peripheral smooth and striated muscles; sympathetic innervation decreases it, like potassium and calcium respectively in the frog experiment. On the other hand, the vagus (depressor nerve) slows down the heart to *diastolic* standstill; the sympathetic (accelerator nerve) acts on the heart muscle in a manner opposite to its effect on peripheral muscle. That is, it heightens its activity and tone, and, when hyperstimulated, brings the heart to *systolic* standstill. Furthermore, the vagal effect can be decreased or even stopped by the addition of calcium, and enhanced by the addition of potassium. The sympathetic effect on the muscle can be neutralized by the addition of potassium—further proofs of the functional identity of the vegetative nervous system and certain antagonistic ion groups. The tonic effect of digitalis can be blocked by potassium and enhanced by calcium, as the former paralyzes the heart, while the latter stimulates it. A surplus of calcium in the tissues produces H-ion dissociation; a potassium surplus produces OH-ion dissociation. An H-ion surplus means death of the tissue. Of potentially great importance to our understanding of vegetative functions are the following findings of Kraus: potassium (that is, the hydro*philic* ion) predominates in the epithelium; calcium (the hydro*phobic*, water-repelling ion) predominates in connective tissue—as does potassium in growth and calcium in age. In cancer tissue, potassium as well as calcium are reported to occur abundantly, which might, perhaps, explain the tissue's tendency to proliferation (abundance of potassium!). Findings of this sort allow us to postulate life-affirmative effects in the potassium-ion group and life-destructive ones in the calcium-ion groups.[11] According to Kraus, muscle tone basically is not the expression of any mysterious nerve fluid, but rather a plasmatic *electrolyte turgor*, an expression of saturated muscle charge. Thus growth and increase in strength must rest on conditions whereby more is gained than used up in the process.

On peripheral blood vessels, the vagus has a dilating effect, which increases surface tension, while the sympathetic constricts the vessels, decreasing surface tension. In glands, too, like the submaxillary, there is antagonistic innervation. Thus, according to Claude Bernard, the sympathetic produces sparse, tenacious secretion (calcium is hydrophobic!), while the vagus, by contrast, stimulates ample fluid secretion. Secretion experiments have shown that the increased pressure of the gland parenchyma is due to vagal innervation, specifically to tissue expansion and increased turgor. The latter, according to Kraus, speeds up the blood flow and not (or not *only*) the other way around. Bernard notes that cutting the sympathetic nerve of the neck heightens tissue tonus; this is explained by the ablation of the sympathetic-suppressing effect of the vagus [i.e., the sympathetic unopposed by the vagus].

The Antithesis between Center and Periphery

Table 2 summarizes the functions of sympathetic and parasympathetic nervous systems, which together are called the "vegetative" [or autonomic] nervous system. The summary is from Müller's *Lebensnerven und Lebenstriebe* (Berlin: Springer, 1931, 3rd ed.).

Table 2

Sympathetic System	Effect on		Parasympathetic System
Relaxation of pupil constrictors, excitation of pupil dilators	− Smooth muscle of iris	+	Excitation (pupil constriction)
Inhibition	− Tear glands	+	Stimulation
Inhibition	− Salivary gland	+	Stimulation
Stimulation	+ Facial sweat glands	−	Inhibition
Constriction (pallor)	+ Blood vessels	−	Dilatation (erythema)
Excitation piloerection	+ Piloerector muscles	−	Relaxation of piloerectors
Dilatation, relaxation	− Bronchial muscles	+	Constriction, tension
Excitation, acceleration	+ Heart muscle	−	Inhibition, deceleration
Inhibition	− Esophagus	+	Stimulation, contraction

Inhibition of function	− Stomach, pancreatic gland, small intestines, kidney, large intestine, rectum	+	Stimulation
Stimulation of adrenalin secretion	+ Adrenal	−	Inhibition
Detrusor inhibition	− Bladder	+	Contraction, urine expulsion
Excitation, closing	+ Sphincter muscle of bladder	−	Inhibition, opening
Penis flaccidity (vasoconstriction)	− Male genitals	+	Penis enlargement, erection, vasodilatation
Inhibition of female sex glands (vasoconstriction)	− Female genitals	+	Vasodilatation, excitation
Excitation	+ Sweat glands of buttocks	−	Inhibition
Excitation	+ Scalp muscles	−	Inhibition
Excitation	+ Smooth muscles of scrotum	−	Inhibition

The table illustrates the great diversity of innervation in the various organs. Sometimes it is the parasympathetic that stimulates muscles, sometimes the sympathetic. Thus the bowel and stomach musculature is stimulated by the parasympathetic and inhibited by the sympathetic, while in the heart the opposite prevails. Though, in general, the sympathetic relaxes the smooth musculature, it contracts the muscles of the peripheral vessels and causes vasoconstriction. Note that the sympathetic inhibits the salivary glands, but stimulates the adrenals, while the vagus acts in exactly the opposite way. It is of particular interest that, in one and the same organ, for example the bladder, the sympathetic stimulates the muscle that prevents urine passage, but relaxes the muscle that expels the urine by a squeezing action; and the parasympathetic does the opposite. The retractor muscle of a dog's penis is stimulated, not relaxed, by the sympathetic; the same applies to the smooth musculature of the human testes. On the other hand, the smooth muscle of the iris dilates [the pupil] under [sympathetic] stimulation, and contracts it when the [sympathetic] is inhibited. The parasympathetic does the opposite.

It would seem as though the laws of innervation are completely arbitrary. Up to now, physiology has formed no opinion on the matter, at least as far as I can judge from the available literature. And yet we may postulate that the "irregularity" of the innervation is only an apparent one, and that it has, nonetheless, a certain lawfulness. Along with the sympathetic and parasympathetic innervation, there is a *functional unity* of the two systems which we can understand only on the basis of the organism's *function as a whole*.

Table 3 is based on this functional unity.

Table 3

Vegetative Group (Mutual enhancement and interchangeability)	General Effect on Tissue	Central/Peripheral

Sympathetic
Calcium (group)
Adrenalin
Cholesterol
OH-ions
	Lowering of surface
	  tension
	Water expulsion
	  (hydrophobic)
	Striated muscle: relaxed
	Decreased susceptibility
	  to electrical stimulation
	Increased O_2 consumption
	Increased blood pressure
		Systolic/vasoconstriction
		Heart muscle stimulation
		Intestinal inhibition

Vagus
Potassium (group)
Choline
Lecithin
H-ions
	Increased surface tension
	Water absorption
	  (swelling of tissues)
	Tetanic contraction of
	  muscle
	Increased susceptibility
	  to electrical stimulation
	Decreased O_2 consumption
	Decreased blood pressure
		Diastolic/dilatation
		Heart muscle relaxation
		Intestinal stimulation

In the sympathetic group's effects, we again come upon anxiety; in the vagus group's effects, sexual excitation. The vagus (sexual) effect is, essentially, the function of organ expansion and peripheral tension; the sympathetic (anxiety) effect is, essentially, the function of peripheral contraction and central tension—if we consider not the individual organs, but the organism's total functioning. The periphery and the center are in an antagonistic functional relationship to each other; expansion and contraction, as basic functions, govern the innervation-as-a-whole of the organism.

The following facts are summarized in Table 3:

1. The antithesis of potassium (vagus) and calcium (sympathetic) groups: expansion and contraction.

2. The antithesis of periphery and center, with respect to excitation.

3. The functional identity of the sympathetic or vagal functions with their chemical stimulus substances.

4. The dependence of organ innervation on the functional unity and antithesis of the organism as a whole.

To begin with, a whole series of hitherto unexplained physiological phenomena are made clear by the functional antithesis of center and periphery. For example, the vagus inhibits the heart but stimulates the voluntary muscles, while the sympathetic, by contrast, stimulates and contracts the heart but inhibits the muscles: the functional connection is shown only if one considers the musculature as part of the periphery of an organism and the heart as part of the center. Every fright reaction shows this antithesis: paralysis of the muscles of the extremities and stimulation of the heart. Here we already see the functions of the organism not bound to separate organs, but to a common lawfulness governing the organism as a whole, an arrangement in which the organs are merely a means to the end. It is not the excitation of a nerve that causes movement; rather, an impulse of the organism as a whole, concretely represented in its functional unity (plasma syncytium), brings its message to the nerve, in accordance with its direction and function. This does not in any way lead us into teleology or the assumption of a hyperindividual entelechy. For, we now see also that the functional unity of the multicelled organism derives from the functional unity of the unicelled organism. Both show the same two basic lawful characteristics of expansion and contraction, not only in their functional relationships, but also in the means and organs involved in performing the functions. In both cases, there is the genetic-functional identity of plasma and blood, plasma and nerves, plasma and muscles. It remains to be seen whether the developmental theory can confirm this functional identity. In any event, it seems physiologically demonstrated that, in plasma, the same inorganic substances (potassium and calcium) and the same organic substances (lecithin and cholesterol) perform the functions of expansion and contraction later fulfilled by the collective morphology of the vegetative (vagus-sympathetic) nervous system. The antithesis of the two basic functions is continued in the antithesis of the vagal-sympathetic innervation. The vagus is, essentially, the system of peripheral excitation and central discharge, that is, of iibidinal *expansion*—psychologically, the direction "toward the world." The sympathetic is essentially the system of peripheral discharge and central excitation, that is, of anxious *drawing into oneself*—psychologically, the direction "away from the world—back into the self."

At this point, the antithesis between sexuality and anxiety can also be placed in the overall view of organic natural phenomena. Anxiety, as a psychic affect, is neither an "expression" nor a "result" nor an "accompaniment" of the sympathetic crawling-back-into-the-self, but a direct inner perception of the process, functionally identical with it. Likewise, sexual pleasure, in its entire gamut, from the simplest state of relaxed well-being to the height of sexual excitement, is the inner perception of the vagal function of reaching out or expansion, which goes hand in hand with the increase in surface tension, mechanically and electrophysiologically. It is the inner perception of fusion and merging with the world, of fully stepping out of oneself; it is functionally identical with what happens physiologically. In this sense, and in this sense only, does it seem possible to understand the body-mind problem; and the separation, in principle, of the so-called functional from the so-called organic nature of illness becomes untenable. The differences are only in the mode of approach of pathogenic stimuli or in the vulnerable points of a person's biosystem. Illnesses begin sometimes as toxic, traumatic, or physiochemical irritations; at other times, as a social inhibition of the individual's psychic motility. They achieve the same effect: a disturbance of the individual's energy equilibrium. In this light, for example, we see schizophrenia neither as "psychogenic" nor "somatogenic," but solely as a disturbance, somehow induced, of basic vegetative functions that are essential for life.

Antithetical in their *direction* of flow and, concomitantly, antithetical in psychic experience, sexuality and anxiety have, so to speak, sprung from a *single* source; moreover, the specific excitations of anxiety and sexuality can change into one another, or even fully supplant one another. They are, therefore, not absolute opposites, but relative ones, identical even in their antithesis. During anxiety and sexual pleasure, the sensations in the region of the celiac ganglion (diaphragm and heart) are, initially, scarcely distinguishable from one another. Only the further course of the excitation determines whether the development is to be toward anxiety or sexual pleasure.

A new view of phenomena and processes deserves careful consideration only when it makes possible the discovery of a common denominator for a series of facts, hitherto unexplained, or explained only with the help of multiple hypotheses. This principle of natural scientific research must also be demonstrated in our hypothesis. As for its consequences, I am fully aware of their extent, though they cannot be adequately surveyed at this time.

The Orgasm as an Electrophysiological Discharge*

1. A Review of Present-day Knowledge

It is only in recent years that physiologists, for the first time, have begun to focus attention on the orgasm phenomenon—the key factor in sex-economic theory. But, since the psychic aspects of the orgastic process are either wholly neglected or psychologically oversimplified, any purely phenomenological description completely misses the mark. Müller, in his collected writings, *Die Lebensnerven* (Springer, 1930, 3rd ed.), certainly refers to the relationship between orgasm and smooth muscle contraction but makes no mention at all of disturbances in orgastic function or the process of physiological excitation. I know of no existing animal or human experiments dealing with this problem, though they are easy to implement—easier than many. In the literature of sexology, many disturbances are described, but their relationship to unconscious psychic processes, sexual physiology, and sociological determinants of sex life is not entirely understood. In psychoanalytic writing, the function of the orgasm was not dealt with until 1925. Therefore, from 1923 to 1927, I undertook to integrate the clinical data on orgasm obtained from psychoanalysis and what was already known about sexual functioning in general. In my book *Die Funktion des Orgasmus* (1927), I brought orgastic function and the phenomenon of anxiety into close functional relationship, each to the other, and both to the autonomic nervous system. After I set forth these fundamental hypotheses, no mention of them appeared in the literature of psychoanalysis or physiology, and only in very narrow circles was any attempt made to integrate my orgasm theory into existing studies of neurosis (Fenichel, *Spezielle Neurosen-*

*Translated from "Der Orgasmus als elektrophysiologische Entladung," *Zeitschrift für Politische Psychologie und Sexualökonomie*, I, 1934.

lehre, 1932). This seemed to illustrate the well-known scientific tradition of giving the silent treatment to certain kinds of discoveries. However, in case my orgasm theory one day proves to have deeper significance, I should prefer to forestall future embarrassment by ascribing this neglect to some lack in my presentation of the problem during the past eight years.

I will summarize briefly the concepts I had already developed at that time as to how the orgastic process works. The orgasm corresponds to a change in concentration of the vegetative excitation; this excitation is transferred from the autonomic nervous system to the sensorimotor system. During the course of the excitation, we may distinguish the following phases: 1) a tension-free accumulation of sexual energy in the vegetative system; 2) a spontaneous or voluntary concentration of this sexual excitation in the genital system (with developing sexual tension and vasomotor activity); 3) advancing involvement of the sensory system (excitation of the erogenous zones; fore-pleasure and pre-orgastic phase of coitus); 4) transfer of excitation to the motor system (muscle tension at the climax and involuntary muscular contractions); and 5) ebbing of excitation in the vegetative system (quiescence: genital and sensorimotor systems relaxed).

The completeness of the orgasm and the orgastic release itself depend directly upon the amount of sexual excitation concentrated at the genitals and the thoroughness of its ebbing away from the vegetative system.

I had already distinguished a *centrifugal* and *centripetal* direction of flow from the beginning to the end of the orgastic excitation. The question as to what kind of excitation could undergo such a change of direction and transfer from the autonomic to other body systems remained unanswered, along with many others.

Moreover, our clinical and psychoanalytic observations on neurosis and sexual disturbances pointed to the following: the orgasm itself appeared to be an excitation phenomenon culminating in a complete reduction of psychic activity and mediated through a basic process of tension and relaxation of the vegetative system. We came to recognize orgastic potency as the ability to release tension adequately through elimination of all inhibitions and to experience this release in the ego.

The above description deals only with the phenomenology

of the orgasm and does not include certain basic aspects of the process. The following questions must still be clarified:

Is sexual tension based only on a mechanical phenomenon?

Is the psychoanalytic concept of libido stasis based on a similar mechanism?

Is the orgastic release of tension a mechanical discharge, perhaps, as many believe, the result of emptying the engorged seminal vesicles or vas deferens, or is it based on some mechanical change in the surface tension of the sex organs?

These and other related questions must be answered, since neither therapy nor prophylaxis of the neuroses is possible, in a sex-economic sense, without their adequate solution. If, as sex economy maintains, orgastic potency is the key to understanding the *economy* and dynamics of psychic life and psychic disturbances, knowledge of the neuroses should throw light on the orgasm problem, and vice versa.

2. Some Unusual Features of Sexuality

Assuming that the process of sexual tension and relaxation has a simple mechanical basis leaves many observations unexplained; these, however, easily fit together, if, in addition to a mechanical process of tension release, we postulate the occurrence of *an electrophysiological discharge during orgasm*. This should be experimentally demonstrable.

First, the concept of *mechanical tension* is only fully applicable to the male, since it *fails to account for what happens in the female*. From a mechanical concept such as this, one could easily conclude, as most sexologists do, that lack of orgasm is natural in the female. The sociological origin of this concept has been amply described elsewhere.[1] The unmistakable appearance of orgastic phenomena in the healthy female—completely equivalent to that of the male—therefore requires explanation. She shows the same kind of movements as the male: rhythmic, clonic contractions of the involuntary musculature; also the same preacme peripheral concentration of excitation and postacme centripetal ebbing of excitation, exactly like the male's.

In coitus interruptus, the mechanical discharge may be complete, and the excitement during acme even greater than usual. Nevertheless, the experience remains unsatisfying, and the feeling of relief from tension is either lacking or incomplete.

In coitus condomatus, the male has full mechanical discharge, but the feeling of satisfaction is greatly reduced. The decrease in tactile sensation *cannot* account for this, since the simple sense of touch is still present; what is missing or diminished is the feeling of pleasure. It is precisely this fact that needs explanation. The role of the tactile pleasure receptors on the nerve end does not explain much, and is itself questionable and in need of much further clarification. In addition, the unmistakable signs of stasis, such as irritability, nervousness, and lack of pleasure in one's work—so often associated with coital use of a condom—attest to the absence of an adequate discharge of tension.

Analytic interviews reveal that in both monogamous and polygamous intercourse, *two basically different sensations arise from tactile excitation*, depending on the type of vaginal secretion produced. Patients describe one type of secretion as "watery," "slippery," or "runny"; the other as "oily," "thick," and "abundant." The former produces a weaker, qualitatively different sensation than the latter. Apparently they correspond, respectively, to the more serous or more colloidal secretions of the female genital glands.

The most striking fact is the relationship between *genital friction and contraction of the genital musculature*, the tonicity of which is greatly increased during erection. But, in addition, every friction movement brings on an involuntary contraction if one does not consciously tighten against it. As friction increases, the involuntary muscle contractions increase in intensity until, as the climax approaches, these are transformed into a rapid series of spontaneous and uncontrollable *clonic spasms*, which pursue their course even though the friction movement has ceased.

If friction brings the contractions to the clonic stage, it may—even before this stage—produce contractions of otherwise voluntarily innervated muscles, such as abdomen, face, and upper and lower extremities. This most essential aspect of "the diffusion of excitation through the entire body" has been referred to previously in the purely phenomenological description of the orgasm.

We must still account for the fact that orgastically impotent, compulsive characters feel no sexual gratification, despite the capacity for mechanical release. We must also explain why, in patients suffering from ejaculatory impotence, genital friction appears to produce no corresponding muscle contractions in vas deferens and pelvic floor.

Very striking and hitherto unexplained (except by recourse to mysticism) is the fact that *a special kind of sexual resonance* can occur between a man and a woman—that is, an attraction later confirmed by a harmony of sexual rhythm. It may happen at the very first glance, though neither are yet aware of it.

Let us remove this "resonance" from the realm of genitality, which cannot account for it—nor can any single qualities of mind or appearance of the partners. We are then left with a certain something, which in popular parlance is called "radiating sex appeal" or having "sexual magnetism." Such a spontaneous, mostly unconscious object choice usually turns out to be harmonious—barring complicating difficulties. The question still remains, however, as to what constitutes this "harmony."

When the erect male organ touches the moist mucous membrane of the vagina, there arises an almost irresistible *urge for complete contact* between the two organ surfaces. The man feels this as an urge to penetrate fully; the woman, to receive completely. In contrast to this "genital magnetism," so to speak, we find this urge greatly diminished or completely absent in orgastically impotent men and frigid women, despite the presence of vaginal lubrication. There may even be a deliberate wish, fully conscious, to avoid penetration and pull out. Another striking feature is that the penis has to overcome a certain resistance in order to withdraw. This can result in a sensation of unpleasure or actual pain. It is particularly intense if withdrawal takes place during acme, at the peak of the excitation, at which point the pleasurable muscular contractions turn into pain. The same thing happens in patients who consciously or unconsciously tighten their pelvic musculature during coitus and are then overwhelmed by the excitation. Such people tend to develop great anxiety prior to intercourse or sexual excitation.

If the vagina is dry, intercourse gives no pleasure at all, or a mild tactile pleasure at best, even when the friction movements lead to a mechanical release in the male.

Masturbation is less satisfying when done with a dry hand than with a saliva-moistened hand; the therapist might bear this in mind when treating patients with disturbed potency. Likewise, if the inside of a condom is moistened before use, a greater sensation is felt.

There is no simple way to explain why slow and gentle friction produces much stronger sensation than harsh and rapid movements. Purely tactile-mechanical explanations do not suffice. Carefully recorded sex histories from analytic subjects reveal that there are two types of genital friction movements: one is a deliberate straining and pushing of the entire torso; the other, a more spontaneous, undulating movement arising from the pelvis itself. We find the first type in people with heightened muscle tonus, or in affect-blocked types, who have to exert conscious effort to overcome their vegetative inhibitions, etc. The second kind occurs only in people who are muscularly relaxed and psychically unblocked. The first type we know is a substitute for *spontaneous* movement. But the meaning of the second type requires further explanation. In a similar vein is the question of why individuals with strongly erotic natures but lacking free-flowing sexuality may feel themselves as unattractive.

Finally, we have to point out one additional hiatus in our understanding of the complex orgasm phenomenon: after orgastic release, the genitals suddenly become refractory to any further excitation, and it becomes impossible to evoke a mental image of the sex act, or at best such images are completely drained of emotion. It is untenable to attribute this to a mechanical release of tension based on vascular engorgement of the genital organs, since the hyperemia abates only very gradually. It appears to be a direct *result* of the sudden drop in genital excitability rather than its cause. In order to explain this phenomenon in neurological terms, one would have to clarify how the end-organ receptors suddenly lose their receptivity right after climax.

All of the above considerations irresistibly point to the assumption that the orgasm represents *a form of electrical discharge*. To my knowledge, this is a concept new to the field of science, though it may have occurred here and there as a popular notion. We must now consider to what extent genital function can support this hypothesis. If this holds up, we must then explore and consolidate the relationship between mechanical relaxation and electrical discharge.

3. Mechanical Tension—Electrical Charge—Electrical Discharge— Mechanical Relaxation

The orgastic function must be an integral part—and a very elementary one at that—of the world of nature. It contains in clear form the basic functions of all living substance: tension, relaxation, charge and discharge, as well as the two fundamental directions of flow of vegetative excitation, which will require further careful elaboration. The orgastic discharge brings a feeling of pleasure and merging with the love object, its blockage leads to anxiety and a feeling of isolation. It holds the key to an understanding of the life-mind problem.

The prime feature in orgastic function is the vegetative excitation of the genital tract. Erection is basically a hyperemia of the genital blood vessels, particularly of the genital arteries (vagal innervation). The genital musculature (ischiocavernosus and bulbocavernosus muscles) is also under vagal stimulation and responds with increased tonus. This causes compression of the penile venous system, which is more superficially located than the penile arteries. The resultant backup of blood produces the erection. (Anxiety is the opposite process: sympatheticotonic innervation contracts the arteries, relaxes the genital musculature, and results in a loss of erection.) The more completely vagal excitation takes over, the more strongly it compresses the urethra and bladder; in other words, the stronger the tone of the peripheral genital muscles, the stronger the ensuing contractions that force the semen past the muscle and vascular barriers.

In the female, the erectile process follows the same principle as in the male: arterial hyperemia and secondary venous engorgement of the corpora cavernosa clitoridis and bulbo vestibuli (the vascular spaces around the clitoris and anterior vaginal wall).

We must therefore distinguish the following components in the process of *mechanical tension*: in the male, *tension in the seminal vesicles and the vas deferens*; in both sexes, a *heightened tension of the tissues themselves* (secondary to increased turgor of the genital glands and tissues), tension resulting from *engorgement* of the corpora cavernosa, and surface tension in the *skin* and *mucous membranes*.

The well-known feeling of genital tension during sexual excitement has a direct mechanical basis, the increasing vegetative tension of the tissues themselves. Clinical studies of sexual disturbances, particularly in women, reveal that every *voluntary* tensing of the striated genital musculature either blocks or hinders sexual satisfaction. We know from the above formulation that the release of mechanical tension is quantitatively proportional to the intensity of the excitation. Therefore, the more relaxed the organism is (apart from purely vegetative tension), the greater is the pleasure experienced from this release.

The next question is—how does mechanical relaxation come about after vagal excitation has led to mechanical tension? Let us recall our earlier observation that genital friction movements result in *involuntary* contractions of both the smooth and striated musculatures.

Every friction movement, i.e., every change in surface contact between the vaginal mucosa and the penile surface, leads to a muscular contraction in healthy individuals. During resting contact or in the absence of movement, no contractions develop (except at the end stage); the tonus may even drop slightly.

We know that galvanic stimuli, both "make" and "break" currents, produce contractions in muscle tissue. Striated muscle gives a rapid contractile response and relaxes just as quickly when the stimulus ceases; on the other hand, smooth muscle reacts with long, drawn-out undulations. It appears unmistakable that muscle contractions occurring with genital friction movements have the same characteristics as those due to electrical stimulation.

As the friction movements mount in frequency and intensity,

the waves of contraction increase; as the climax is reached, tetany occurs—exactly as if induced by a rapid series of electrical stimuli—that is, a prolonged spasm at the peak of contraction. This tetany is then released with or without further friction movement by a series of *clonic contractions*, that is, by involuntary, automatic contractions of the entire genital musculature. It is not the tetanic contraction, but rather the ensuing clonus which brings about orgasm and the release of tension; the convulsive movements diminish and give way to a feeling of complete relaxation and subsequent drowsiness. It is now clear what ejaculation and release of tension entail. Under the stimulus of friction movements, a generalized excitation or tension is built up; during orgasm, this is released by a series of spontaneous muscular contractions which are independent of stimulation. The energy charge is dissipated and quiescence follows.

It is left to the physiologists to check these facts, make any necessary revisions, and determine exactly *what kind* of electrical activity is actually involved. At present, we are satisfied with the insight that an electrical discharge is present. The strong clonic contractions resulting from this discharge empty the seminal vesicles against the resistance of the tonically narrowed penile musculature and bring about a secondary, mechanical discharge. *Just as, before, mechanical tension was needed for an electrical charging of the genitals, now an electrical discharge is necessary for mechanical relaxation.* Since this reciprocal interplay between electrical and mechanical activity is an essential feature of the orgastic process, let us distinguish the *"tension-charge"* and *"discharge-relaxation" reactions* that, taken together, constitute the orgasm.

In order for there to be a complete feeling of release and satisfaction, it is not the mechanical but the electrical discharge that is essential, as the following discussion will make clear. Even minimal electric charges are sufficient to cause an evacuation of the seminal vesicle. However, the *feeling of gratification* does not depend upon seminal evacuation, but rather is proportional in intensity *to the prior mechanical tension, to the ensuing electrical charge, and to the amount of resistance that has to be overcome during the transition to clonus.* Accordingly, when ejaculation occurs during sleep, or during partial erection, there is little or no feeling of pleasure and relaxation; the completeness of release depends directly on the strength of the preceding erective tension. It also follows that one of the essential features of orgastic potency is the rhythm and force of the ejaculation, and not merely its occurrence.

We can now understand why coitus condomatus is wholly or partially unsatisfactory, even though a mechanical release of tension takes place. Clearly, the buildup of electrical charge is deficient, since the friction movements in this case are less pleasurable; but, above all, the preacme muscular contractions fail to occur and culminate in tetany. The clonic spasms are less intense, fewer in number, and weaker than normal. Thus coital use of the condom raises a very important question as to how the electrical excitation is discharged, where it is localized, and what direction it takes in the two sexual partners.

We must therefore postulate the setting-up of an electrical system in each partner respectively, and we must ask how each of these systems is related to the other; since excitation and gratification depend precisely on this reciprocal relationship, which involves tactile as well as other factors.

For a clearer understanding, let us recall the setup and functioning of a simple electrolytic system.

If we fill a glass container with dilute hydrochloric acid and introduce two platinum electrodes connected to [opposite poles of] an electric power source (but not to each other), an electric current will flow through the solution. If we connect the electrodes together with a good conductor, such as an iron wire, this produces a short circuit and the current bypasses the solution. However, if the current is passed into the solution, electric charges accumulate at each electrode. Soon we note that chlorine (anion) collects at the anode (positive pole) and hydrogen (cation) at the cathode (negative pole). According to Arrhenius's theory, the hydrochloric acid molecule does not decompose, but rather, each component atom is oppositely charged (chlorine negatively, hydrogen positively) and bound to a positive and negative ion, respectively. The electrodes constitute two *surface boundaries* that carry a strong charge when the circuit is connected. Then, according to the theory, the negative chloride ions and positive hydrogen ions lose their originally random distribution in solution and become attracted to the oppositely charged electrode. The hydrogen (positive) ions go to the negative terminal (cathode) while the chloride (negative) ions go to the positive terminal (anode); at these electrodes, their ionic charge becomes neutralized and they are transformed into uncharged atoms. Thus, in the foregoing process of electrolysis, the charges of the cathode and anode do not directly neutralize each other, but do so through the intermediary of the positively and negatively charged ions present in the electrolytic solution.

We know, furthermore, that when two fluids are separated by a membrane or by a boundary surface (as the interface between two immiscible liquids is called), an electric surface potential is generated. If two such surface potentials are separated by a conducting fluid medium, ionic currents arise. This results in an equalization of the potential difference and a cancellation of the charge.

Pure water, a nonconductor, is not an electrolyte. Saliva, on the other hand, is a conductor. Thus, not by chance, clinical material reveals that erotic sensations are greatly reduced if the vaginal mucosa is moistened with water; with saliva, sensation is more intense, though not nearly so great as with the vaginal secretion, which is a colloidal acid solution.

As we know, the intensity of the pleasure sensation depends upon the proportion of watery to colloidal secretion. "Watery" secretion produces less pleasure than a "thicker," "oilier" one. How does this fit into our overall scheme?

First, the arrangement of membranes, boundary surfaces, and fluids during coitus points to the presence of a complete electrolyte system.

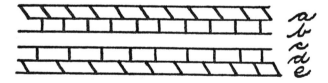

(a) male circulation
(b) male boundary layer (penile epidermis)
(c) female secretions (conducting medium)
(d) female boundary layer (vaginal mucosa)
(e) female circulation

We may consider the penile and vaginal surfaces as the two boundary surfaces or electrodes of the system. The acid vaginal secretion (which is an electrolyte) represents the contact medium (or conductor) between the two surfaces. The male and female circulations and the mutually stimulating plasmatic excitations in the autonomic nervous system represent the inherent sources of electrical charge on the organs of sexual contact. The equalization of the potential gradient occurs *between the two surface potentials: penile epidermis* and *vaginal mucosa.* In this scheme, we must distinguish three separate electrical phases: 1) the electric current generated by the male circulation; 2) the corresponding current in the female; 3) the electrolytic equalization of their respective charges through genital contact. The latter process must occur by means of ionic convection through the vaginal secretions, with the genital surfaces acting as electrodes. To support these assumptions, the following would be required:

1. Demonstration of the electrolytic properties of the vaginal secretions (electrical resistance, ionic composition, etc.).

2. Demonstration that the genital surfaces really are the locus of buildup of potential. (In this connection, the following should also be shown: the potential difference between the erect and flaccid organ; the relationship between amount of engorgement and degree of electrical charge; the reaction of the erect organ to an artificial electrode; and the ability of an intact skin or mucosal surface to discharge electrically.)

3. Demonstration of the polarity of charge, negative or positive, of the male and female surface potentials, respectively.

4. An experimental study of the electrolytic potential of various subjects according to their character structure, with special reference to the sexually disturbed female.

If we regard the sex act as basically an electrical process, we are able to understand the phenomenon of genital magnetism, as well as the muscular contractions produced by friction movement. According to physical laws, the extent to which a potential gradient between two charged surfaces can be equalized depends directly on the completeness of their mutual contact. By the same token, neutralization will be less extensive if the contact is less complete. The impulse toward *complete* contact of the genital surfaces, that is, toward complete penetration followed by complete separation, we can explain by the following events: the partial release of tension occurring during genital contact and the rebirth of tension occurring when the organs are separated. We may thus distinguish two different kinds of *pleasure sensation*: the first stems from the *partial* release of tension occurring during friction-free contact; this is a precursor of the final orgastic pleasure in which the total charge is spent and the tension fully released; the second type occurs during friction contact, as a result of stimulation and the associated muscle contractions. Likewise, this motoric pleasure, surely the archetype of all motor-derived muscular pleasure, is an anticipation of the process that culminates in orgastic clonus. Let us call the first kind *"relaxation pleasure"* and the second *"tension pleasure."* Essentially, the former comes from a *decrease* and the latter from an *increase* in the surface potential gradient. The process is unequivocally clear with regard to the motionless phases of coitus, where there is anticipatory release of tension, as well as to the postorgastic phase when such release has been totally accomplished.

We are less clear in regard to the basis of "tension pleasure." According to our theories, tension should be experienced as unpleasure, not pleasure, which usually is the expression of a reduction in tension. The tension mounts somewhat after a friction movement, but abates considerably when the genitals rest together motionless; this permits a further rise in tension during the next friction movement, which is once again experienced as pleasurable. How can this ongoing increase of tension be reconciled with the accompanying feeling of pleasure ("tension pleasure")? Certainly each new friction movement increases the electric surface potential; but at the same time, the ensuing spasmodic muscle contractions discharge this accumulated energy, and *it is these contractions which render the experience of increasing tension as pleasurable rather than unpleasurable.*

There are two observations to support this hypothesis. First, Kraus concluded experimentally (without relating it to our problem) that a nerve under excitation *builds up* tension while a muscle under excitation *discharges* it through contraction.

During friction movement, both the contacting surfaces and the autonomic nervous system are becoming charged with energy, while at the same time, genital muscle contractions are releasing energy.

According to this, forepleasure consists of a simultaneous charge plus *partial* discharge. It was on this very concept that, in 1923, I based the phenomenological description of the sex act in my article "Zur Triebenergetik."[2] According to this, forepleasure is seen as a *dialectic* process, by which we may explain how a rise in tension can be pleasurable. Secondly, we find that, during genital friction, masochistic perverts experience the buildup of pleasure as unpleasure, and are compelled to avoid the *heightening* of pleasure sensations. At the same time, we find that a basic characteristic of sexual masochists is the *voluntary* contraction of the genital musculature in order to avoid the involuntary muscular contractions. This shows that if the latter are suppressed, the friction movement itself becomes merely an unpleasurable process of charge (like a continuous tickling stimulus) and will therefore be avoided.

In contrast to forepleasure, the final orgastic pleasure is a pure pleasure process and comes entirely from the muscular discharge; the muscular contractions discharge the nervous excitation by a process not entirely clear at the present time. The latter assumption is inescapable, since after orgasm the nervous system is refractory to further excitation and no further charging of the autonomic system is possible for a certain amount of time, whether by friction or fantasy; the surface of the genitals is not excitable either. However, the potential for a new buildup of charge is directly dependent on this discharge. This is seen in the greater orgastic potency resulting from regular, satisfying sexual activity, and its disturbance when satisfaction is seldom forthcoming.

In the frigid woman, deliberate tensing of the entire musculature suppresses involuntary muscle contractions, while dryness of the vaginal mucosa prevents the buildup of charge from friction movement.

How much of this dysfunction is psychogenic and how much is autonomic in origin will be discussed elsewhere.

In patients suffering from premature ejaculation, the genital musculature may reach too quickly the point of involuntary spasms (jerky ejaculation) or may simply fall into a state of tonic involuntary contraction (seminal emission only). In such cases, the excitation is transferred too soon from the autonomic nervous system to the musculature; physiologically, the actual process is still a mystery.

Furthermore, in both sexes one can discern differences in

sexual behavior based on differences in orgastic potency. I should like to summarize them briefly here and try to consider their implications carefully with regard to sexual mores.

It is apparent that individuals who can experience friction-induced orgastic convulsions are much more likely to be monogamous than those whose sensations come only from mechanical discharge. The former have no need to inhibit polygamous impulses or follow moralistic codes; rather, their monogamy stems from the wish to repeat a vital, satisfying experience, in accordance with sex-economic principles. Naturally, this presupposes complete sexual harmony between the partners. There is no difference in this regard between men and women. On the other hand, if a suitable partner is not available, as so often happens under present sexual circumstances, the capacity for monogamy shows its opposite side in a tireless search for the right sex object. Polygamous behavior thus motivated cannot be considered neurotic, though prolonged sexual stasis can lead to neurosis. This questing activity does not arise from sexual repression but, on the contrary, is the expression of natural sexual impulses. After an appropriate partner is found, monogamous behavior is automatically resumed and lasts as long as the relationship is harmonious and mutually satisfying. In accordance with sex-economic principles, desires and fantasies concerning other mates are either greatly attenuated or not translated into action. This remains the case as long as no new partner presents an equal or greater appeal than the original mate. However, if the new relationship promises to afford greater pleasure, the earlier one is irrevocably broken off.

These facts run irreconcilably counter to the entire setup of sexual mores in present-day society, where material ties and responsibility toward children are in conflict with principles of sex economy. For this reason, it is precisely the healthiest individuals who suffer the most from sex-negative societal restrictions.

In contrast to this is the behavior of the orgastically disturbed, those who are incapable of electrical charge and discharge. Since they get less pleasure from intercourse, they are in a better position to tolerate the lack of a sex partner for a shorter or longer period, or they are less selective, since the sex act does not mean very much to them. If they are polygamous, it is the result of a sexually disturbed personality structure.

They regularly show more or less deep-seated disturbances in their work capacity, which is not the case among those achieving full orgastic release. They are more able to submit to the restraints of marriage; however, their fidelity is based not on sexual contentment, but on moralistic inhibitions; in other words, not on sex-economic principles but on socially imposed sexual morality. They very easily undergo neurotic regression to infantile conflicts. Their polygamous relationships are scarcely satisfying, and their long-term addiction to this form of activity makes them less and less likely to find an adequate sex partner. They are often in a better position to submit to the demands of bourgeois society but pay for it with various neurotic complaints that take their toll on the entire family group, especially the children. We see clearly right here how the illusion of "hereditary factors" can operate. If such individuals undergo successful analysis and achieve orgastic potency, they modify their behavior and begin to develop all the attributes of the genital character.[3] For sex economy, orgastic impotence holds the key to an economic and dynamic understanding of every kind of neurotic disturbance, symptomatic or characterological. Accordingly, it indicates dysfunction—not in the mechanical tension process (which would correspond to erective impotence)—but in the electrophysiological process of contact, charge, and discharge. The orgastic disturbance is relatively independent of the mechanical processes of hyperemia and surface tension, even though these are essential prerequisites to orgasm.

From all of the foregoing, a host of further questions arises, the most important of which is the following: inasmuch as the orgasm is based upon *elementary* natural principles, we would be extremely interested in determining if the process of tension charge governs the orgastic function alone, or whether, as a universal phenomenon in nature, it represents a basic law of all living functions.

Experimental Investigation of the Electrical Function of Sexuality and Anxiety*

Foreword

The following experimental paper is another in a series of reports dealing with the function of the orgasm and the autonomic life processes. Earlier, as I had anticipated, I was able to demonstrate experimentally this breakthrough into the realm of the autonomic life processes. To understand this report, biologists and physiologists must have some knowledge of my two recent papers: "The Orgasm as an Electrophysiological Discharge" (1934) and "The Basic Antithesis of Vegetative Life Functions" (1934). This paper, as well as its predecessors, should be regarded as a preliminary communication only. I should like to confine myself primarily to a presentation of the purely empirical findings and postpone tying this all up theoretically until I have adequately clarified a whole series of important but unclear findings in the broad and increasingly complex field of sex-economic research.

1. Basic Summary of Clinical Aspects

In my paper "The Orgasm as an Electrophysiological Discharge," I tried to tie together all the clinical data on sexual functioning which would remain incomprehensible unless based

---

*Translated from the monograph *Experimentelle Ergebnisse über die elektrische Funktion von Sexualität und Angst,* Sexpol Press, Copenhagen, 1937.

on an electrical theory of sexuality. According to this view, the process of sexual excitation is an electrical charging of the erogenous zones on the surface of the organism; the orgasm itself is a discharge of the potential built up as a result of preorgastic friction. Furthermore, noting the autonomic excitation that occurs after release of character armor and muscular tension, I came to view sexuality and anxiety as two distinct processes of excitation ("streamings") of the biological organism, which stemmed from the same autonomic source yet moved in diametrically opposite directions. Accordingly, sexuality would encompass everything related to peripherally directed excitation, streaming, energetic charging, and expansion. In essence, it is perceived subjectively as the feeling of pleasure. By contrast, anxiety includes everything related to excitation and flow centrally directed—away from the world. This would correspond to centrally innervated vegetative tension, felt and expressed as "tightening," "oppression," "inner tension," etc. (cf. my paper, "The Basic Antithesis of Vegetative Life Functions").

This hypothesis is based on character-analytic observations and sex-economic principles. It has been confirmed and established in the Psychoanalytic Polyclinic [Vienna] after years of thorough testing. I knew from the start that its full significance would unfold in the field of neurosis and character pathology if one could find experimental support for the clinical phenomena on which it is based.

In the course of putting my theory to the test experimentally, it seemed as though I had stumbled across the core problem of the basic life process itself—as an inevitable outgrowth of my purely clinical observations. For if sexuality and anxiety represent two basic antithetical functions of living matter, we must prove and reproduce this fact experimentally.

From clinical observations on sexuality, I derived the following formula for the function of orgastic excitation: the first stage of sexual excitation is heightened turgor of the tissues, that is, an increase in mechanical tension secondary to blood engorgement; the second stage is an increase in surface electrical charge (rise to acme); the third is the discharge of potential built up during the involuntary muscle contractions; the fourth is the mechanical relaxation following the decrease in hyperemia. The "tension—charge—discharge—relaxation" formula

of the orgasm requires the most careful experimental verifica-
tion. This is especially so because it contains in essence the
fundamental manifestation of life. The orgasm is a basic manifestation of living matter, and the tension-charge formula can
in no way be applied to nonliving phenomena. A survey of
the literature—albeit incomplete—plus exhaustive inquiries to
physicists and physiologists yielded the following information:
in nonliving nature, there exists no process whereby mechanical
tension leads to electrical charge and mechanical relaxation
follows electrical discharge. On first reviewing the clinical data,
I questioned whether this specific dialectic relationship between mechanical and electrical processes demonstrated some
basic principle of biological functioning. The significance of
this question is very clear. The tension-charge formula is, however, only a hypothesis derived from clinical observations and
facts; if it is to lead to more useful theory and practice, it
must be supported experimentally.

Review of Literature

In the available physiological literature, I could find no data
to support the tension-charge formula and the basic autonomic
antithesis of sexuality and anxiety. On the other hand, there
were reports of experiments on the electrical functions of the
skin.

The first report on the skin as a source of an electromotive
force is found in correspondence between C. Ludwig and
DuBois Reymond (*Akad. Verl. Ges.*, 1927). They described
two different types of experiments: those dealing with the skin
as a *conductor* of electricity (variations in resistance) and those
dealing with the skin as a *generator* of electricity (source of
the e.m.f.). H. Rein demonstrated the existence of an electric
potential between closely adjacent skin areas. The skin's ability
to act as an [electrical] membrane was shown by the fact that
whenever the skin under both electrodes is injured, the potential
difference disappears (*Z.f. Biol.* 85, 195, 1926). Philip Keller
demonstrated that the skin potentials undergo continuous
change (*Klinische Wochenschrift* 2, 1081, 1929). C. P. Richter
studied the influence of diurnal and seasonal variations on skin
resistance and found that in normal subjects skin resistance
was lower in the morning than at other times of the day. From

the above experiments, one concludes that fixed "normal" values for the direct current resistance of human skin cannot be established, since the results are extremely variable, fluctuating according to age, sex, experimental setup, diurnal and seasonal factors, etc. (Rein, *Handbuch*). However, Philip Keller was able to demonstrate that under rigorously controlled experimental conditions there were no significant differences among persons of different ages and sex. Interestingly enough, there was a marked negativity of the palm of the hand as compared with other regions of the body (56 mV versus 20-30 mV). Keller further demonstrated that even the most delicate touching of the human skin leads to a completely reversible increase in positive potential of the affected region. In addition, he showed a relationship between skin reaction and that of the sweat glands.

These experiments on the electrical function of the skin neglected to consider its erogenous function—that is, they failed to relate skin reactivity to skin erogenicity and to the affects of sexuality and anxiety. They also failed to investigate how the specifically erogenous zones differ from the rest of the skin. Theoretically, one would expect some attempt to explain the appearance of *local* variations in the skin zones studied. For example, perhaps some process in the sweat glands might be responsible for the increase in positive potential. But this kind of explanation errs by confusing the means of fulfilling a function with the function itself. This would isolate a function which is limited to a certain skin zone and set it apart from the functional unity of the organism as a whole. For example, as was shown, the surface of the hand responds to a shock by becoming negatively charged. One then might try to relate this reaction to a change in the functioning of the sweat glands on the hand. While this is not incorrect, it still obscures the more *basic* fact that when an *organism* is frightened it is the *total organism* which reacts, and, in this case, the surface of the hand represents only a detail of this total functioning.

In considering the results detailed below, it is important to realize the following:

1. The electromotive function of the skin has been established beyond doubt.

2. The skin has the ability to act as a membrane.

3. Normal values for skin potential cannot be fixed.

The theoretical explanation of my experimental results is based on the following concept: the electrical function of the skin is not a purely localized, isolated reaction, but, rather, the expression of a unitary function related to the bioelectric totality of the organism.[1] The skin may be regarded as only a special kind of membrane, since *the total biological organism is composed of a complicated salt electrolyte, colloidal electrolyte, and membrane system.* The relevant literature, especially the fundamental experiments of Kraus, Zondek, and others, I have already cited in my work "The Basic Antithesis of Vegetative Life Functions."

Tarchanoff and Veraguth found that the skin potential varies according to psychic stimulation. I will return to this fact later. Tarchanoff grouped these observations under the term "psychogalvanic response." Clinically, the following facts are significant in the field of psychopathology: the skin reacts electrically under the stimulus of affect; and even more important, there is a functional relationship between the *kind* of affect and the *direction* of electrical charge. The literature on the relationship between autonomic excitation and the emotions is so extensive that it is not possible to give a critical summary here. This will be done elsewhere in a more comprehensive theoretical review of the entire field.

For the present, we need only note that the literature offers no concept of the simultaneous functional identity and antithesis of the emotions and the autonomic apparatus. Rather, the physiological phenomenon is considered an "epiphenomenon" of the affect, or the affect is considered the "result" of an autonomic excitation. Thus the former view regards affect as lacking any objective biophysiological basis, since physiological phenomena are considered only epiphenomena. The latter view is a mechanistic concept which considers affect the "product" of an autonomic excitation. This idea is similar to the neurologists' myth that thinking results from secretions in the brain. Our present hypothesis—namely, that affect and autonomic excitation represent an indivisible and inseparable functional identity, and that the one is inconceivable without the other—opens up a significant perspective for exploring the borderland between psychology and physiology.

Lastly, we must emphasize that our present study brings genital pleasure into the realm of experimental research.

2. Observations with the Oscillograph

In performing the following experiments, we used as our general frame of reference "The Basic Antithesis of Vegetative Life Functions" plus a specific hypothesis that we evolved step by step. These were supported consistently by well-known clinical facts. To avoid error, we set up experimental controls so that our working hypothesis would not bias the results. In the course of the work, there were many occasions where clinical theories seemed inadequate. In essence, it all boiled down to testing the correctness of the postulated "tension-charge" formula, or so-called orgasm formula.

The Biological Resting Potential

The first demonstrable aspect of the electrical function of sexuality is the electrical resting (or ground) potential shown by the *uninjured* skin or mucous membrane surfaces. The literature of the past few years contains an abundance of experimental evidence for this fact. Despite this, knowledge of the electrical surface charge is not well-known even in physiological circles. [The following procedure illustrates the phenomenon.]

Scratch the skin surface of an experimental subject who is hooked up to an oscillograph. Place the ground electrode on the injury site and apply the grid electrode, without pressure, to various intact skin areas. The light tracing on the oscillograph will show a deviation from the previously steady absolute zero line, and will register as a sudden jump to another region of the graph. The electrical surface charge of the uninjured skin has affected the grid potential (read as zero on the tracing), by increasing or decreasing its value. That it is, in fact, the uninjured portion of the skin which is involved in this reaction can easily be demonstrated by the following: if leads from two injury sites are simultaneously connected to the apparatus, there is *no* deviation from the zero line and the light tracing remains absolutely steady.

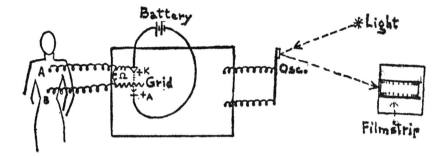

Physical Basis of the Experiments

To understand the experimental results, we need an explanation, albeit simplified, of the physical principle of the apparatus employed. It is based on the fact that a balanced electrical circuit will be affected by the introduction of a human body into the hookup. The effect of this will be manifested by a deviation of the otherwise steady tracing on the oscillographic film record. This tracing is produced by the reflection of a beam of light from a small mirror attached to a thin coil of the oscillograph; the latter is rotated by variations in strength of the electromagnetic field [see the above diagram].

It is most important to understand the relationship between the electrical potential of the human body and that of the apparatus. For this, a quick review of the principle of the vacuum tube amplifier is necessary.

We must first of all understand why an increase in charge of the body surface results in a positive deflection, and a decrease, in a negative deflection. This is related to the working principle of the amplifier tube, whose current is influenced by these changes in charge. The amplifying tube is a vacuum tube inside which a glowing cathode filament is placed opposite a "cold" anode. Between the two is the "grid," a kind of metal screen. The anode and cathode are attached, respectively, to the positive and negative poles of a battery (the "anode battery"). The so-called anode current is defined as a flow of "positive current" from the anode to the cathode. From the heated cathode (or filament), electrons, negatively charged, are emitted and generate a negative current flowing to the grid and then to the anode. The anode has a positive charge, and, since opposite charges attract, it attracts the negatively charged particles emanating from the cathode. Between the anode and cathode there exists a potential difference, the so-called anode potential.

There is also a potential difference between the grid and the cathode, which are connected together by a shunt, to form a secondary circuit. The grid, which is constantly bombarded by the electrons, tends to take on a negative charge. As this occurs, the electron flow is partially repelled by the grid, while the anode, with its positive charge, still continues to attract the remaining electrons. As a result, *the more the grid increases in negative charge (or decreases in positive charge), the more it repels electrons back to the cathode, and the fewer the electrons that reach the anode; therefore, the weaker the current from cathode to anode and the lower the potential difference, or grid potential between the grid and the cathode. Likewise, the less negatively charged (or more positively charged) the grid becomes, the more electrons reach the anode, and the stronger the current becomes.* To recapitulate, the first case (increasing the negative charge of the grid) results in a decreased (anode) current; the second case (increasing the positive charge) results in an increased (anode) current.

If we now connect any two regions of the human body, A and B, to the cathode and grid respectively, thereby completing the circuit, the light tracing either remains steady or is deflected to the left or right. If it remains steady, it means the resting current of the apparatus, that is, the grid potential, has not been affected. This may occur for two reasons: first, the two regions of the body may have the same charge. If there is no difference in charge between them, there is no potential gradient to generate a current. This also occurs when two separate injury sites are connected to the apparatus. If, however, one injury site and one intact site are connected, an electrical gradient will exist between the two. This potential gradient affects the previously constant grid potential, which registers as a steady zero line before the body is hooked up to the circuit. The apparatus is so constructed that the zero line remains at a steady level when the subject is not connected to the apparatus; that is, the current in the apparatus, and therefore the grid potential, remains steady. The zero line is arbitrarily chosen according to the setup of the equipment; therefore, use of another apparatus might result in another set of absolute values if a different zero line were chosen.

If two skin zones have markedly different charges or if one of them is injured, the light beam is deflected from the zero point. If the deflection is to the left (for a given hookup of the oscillograph), the skin zone connected to the grid has a greater charge than that of the grid potential. This results in a potential gradient between the skin and the grid and an increase in the positive charge of the grid. As noted before, this in turn causes an increase in the flow of electrons from cathode to anode, an *increased* current in the apparatus, and an increase in the grid potential: the oscillograph tracing is deflected to the left. On the other hand, when the grid is connected to a skin zone having a lower charge than that of the grid, the grid potential *decreases*. In this case, the grid takes on an increased negative charge, the electrons are repelled, and the current decreases, since fewer electrons can pass through the (relatively more negative) grid to the anode.

In summary: when the grid becomes negative, it indicates a decrease in electrical charge; when positive, an increase in charge.

The choice of the terms "up," "down," "left," or "right" is also an arbitrary one, but must be retained consistently for the entire series of experiments. If the oscillograph connections are reversed or the skin leads connected to the cathode instead of the grid, obviously many of the observed relationships would be reversed. For example, if we wish to indicated "positive" by an upward (or left) deflection, and "negative" by a downward deflection, the positive terminal of the apparatus must be connected to the body zones having a positive charge.

There is also the very important problem of polarization phenomena arising from the use of metal electrodes. We resolved this by installing a two-million-ohm resistance in the circuit between the subject and the vacuum tube, so that for practical purposes there is no actual flow of current, and only the potential differences are measured. Since there is no current flow, there is no polarization. According to the information supplied by the manufacturer, the actual flow of current from the body to the apparatus is of the order of 10^6 mA.

Using the experimental setup described, we measured the

potential of the skin test sites in proportion to the grid potential. Through a series of trials with the same experimental hookups, we determined that all skin sites, with the exception of the easily excitable "ticklish" or "erogenous" zones, had a resting potential in the neighborhood of 10–40 mV. Repeated trials on the same subject gave the same results consistently—that is, variations of 1–5 mV. With certain exceptions, to be noted later, the potential of most of the skin surface was symmetrically equal on corresponding right and left sides of the body.

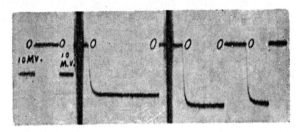

1. Average skin potential

Electrophoto 1 shows the resting potential (RP) of a female subject suffering from hysteria. The potential of the axilla appears the same on the left and the right, about −18 mV., and this is confirmed by a control test. As with all nonerogenous skin zones, a horizontal line results. The electrocardiographic tracing is also present and can be recognized on all of the photographs by its regularity. The direction of the cardiac deflection depends on whether the left or right arm is used as the site of the ground electrode. The reason for this is still unclear. The zero line of the apparatus remains constant.

A uniformly horizontal tracing is characteristic of the *biological resting potential* of the uninjured skin surface of an organism. It shows that *a constant electrical charge is being generated, with only rare fluctuations while at rest, from the interior of the organism to its surface.*

The Resting Potential of the Erogenous Zones

A few skin sites stand out as having a much higher potential than the nonerogenous zones of the body—namely, those which play a leading role in sexual sensitivity and excitability: penis, vaginal mucosa, tongue, inner surface of the lips, anal mucosa, nipple, palm of the hand, earlobe, and, interestingly enough, in some subjects with apparently marked intellectual abilities, the forehead. *These areas are different in their electrical functioning from the rest of the skin surface.* In particular, they have the capacity to register a resting potential much higher—or much lower—than that of other regions. On the latter, I found a resting potential of 0 to about −40 mV. By contrast, the sexual zones repeatedly showed deflections of up to 200 mV or one fifth of a volt; and there are several indications that their uppermost limit of potential has not been fully delineated.

Here we reach a problem which is central to the entire question [of electrical functions].

From clinical experience with psychiatric patients, we know that the sexual zones show a sensitivity and capacity for arousal far surpassing those of the rest of the body. When these functions are intact, one feels them subjectively as sensations of streaming, itching, tingling, pleasurable flushing, etc. The non-erogenous skin surfaces show these qualities to a far lesser degree or not at all. *Now is it possible that the intensity of excitation of a sexual zone corresponds exactly to its electrical charge?* To determine this, a further series of observations is necessary.

The erogenous zones may: 1) have a charging capacity that lies within the limits of variation of the rest of the skin; or 2) far surpass the upper limit of charge of the general skin surface.

A second basic phenomenon shown by the oscillograph may clarify in part these special properties, namely, *the wandering of the light tracing*, that is, the steady, gradual rise or fall of the potential.

The "Wandering" of the Potential

Electrophoto 2 shows the state of electrical charge of a semi-erect penis during the course of half an hour. The scale of the apparatus is adjusted so that a vertical deflection of one centimeter corresponds to 10 mV. The first deflection is about +35 mV, and the second deflection is about double that of

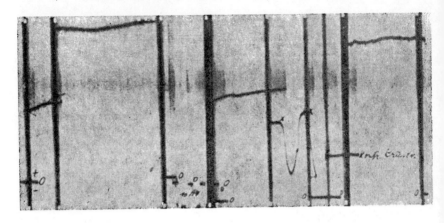

2. Potential of semierect penis

the grid potential arising from an injury site. Control reference to the zero-potential level gives only minor deflections of about 3–4 mV, which are negligible. A third measurement results in a +40 mV deflection: a control test of the nipple gives about +20 mV, and the final measurement of the penis, about +70 mV. The EKG tracing is clear; the zero line remains constant.

The points marked by two crosses and forming a loop down below register a negative potential: this represents the control done by pressing the electrode on the penis. I will return to this point later. We must now grasp two basic facts which are absolutely essential for a correct understanding of the entire problem:

1. *There is no rise in potential unless erotic, streaming sensations accompany the tumescence. The organ can even be fully erect without any rise in potential. The increased potential is always associated with the subjective feeling of pleasure and vice versa*, as will be shown later by other experiments. The original assumption that erection is always associated with increased charge proves to be false. My results would seem to confirm exactly a mechanical-plus-electrical hypothesis: for, evidently, an increased surface charge must be added to the mechanical congestion before a feeling of sexual tension, experienced as pleasurable, can arise.

2. In general, variations in potential height are gradual, not

sudden: figuratively speaking, the potential "wanders" quickly or slowly up and down. Repeated control experiments with inorganic materials show that this slow organic wandering has a special quality, a certain steadiness, easily recognizable with experience. The fact that these changes in potential are reflected in consciousness by changes in the feeling of excitation, of *streaming*, demonstrates an amazing parallelism between the objective, quantifiable events and their subjectively felt intensity. (Control experiments with inorganic substances will be discussed later.)

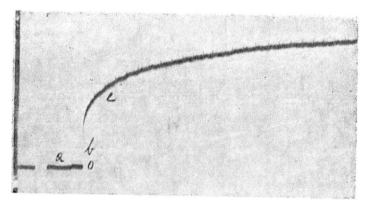

3. "Wandering" of the potential of a palm

Electrophoto 3 shows a weak wandering potential of the left palmar surface of a female hysteric subject. With the electrode resting in place, the potential rises from +15 mV to about +30 mV; the electrocardiogram is visible; the tracing shows only half of the total run; 2.3 mm. of filmstrip equals about a *one*-second interval. The tracing therefore represents changes in potential for a period of about twenty-five seconds. (For a precise gauging of the results, the beginning of the tracing should be disregarded.)

Electrophoto 4 shows the wandering potential of the same palmar surface one day later. The potential reads about +35 mV at the beginning, then rises more steeply than on the previous day; that is, the rise in excitation per unit of time is greater than on the first tracing. This corresponded perfectly

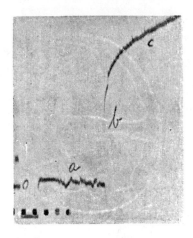

4. Steep rise in potential
of the palm

to the way the patient felt: she was in a much better mood during the second experiment than on the day before.

3. *The rise in potential must be regarded as the response of the organ to the stimulus of gentle touching with the electrode.* However, the intensity of the excitation, as we can show, is related not to the intensity of the stimulus, but rather to the organ's state of excitability, or, better, its readiness to be excited.

Photos 5 and 6 show the excitation of the anal mucosa of a female subject upon contact with the KCl electrode, on two different days:

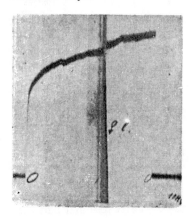

5. Anal mucosa of a
woman in a state of
sexual excitation

Photo 5: here we have wandering potentials of about +25 mV. The subject was in a happy mood, and was particularly interested in knowing what the tracing showed.

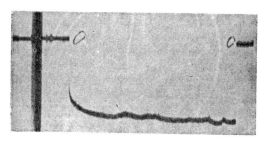

6. The same mucous membrane in a state of
depression (menstruation)

Photo 6: here we have a slight lowering of the potential, which starts out as −15 mV and remains "horizontal."[2]

On the day of the experiment, the subject was in a state of premenstrual depression. Here, too, the type and position of the potential recorded indicates the subject's emotional state. How does this relationship come about?

4. *The wandering potential represents a preorgastic, streaming excitation or discharge.* For a given person, it varies according to his changing emotional states.

5. *The preorgastic potential (POP) of the same erogenous zones varies from person to person.* On the other hand, the resting potential of nonerogenous zones is more or less the same regardless of the subject.

Thus the preorgastic potential sits on the resting potential like a mountain slope on a plain. It bespeaks a heightened biological activity on the periphery of the organism. In order to determine how the *intensity of subjective feeling* is related to the *quantity* of electrical charge, we need a further series of experiments and controls.

Tickling and Pressure Phenomena

Thus far we have examined phenomena that demonstrate the existence of an electrical charge on the periphery of the

organism at various sites and various times without the media-
tion of an external stimulus. That such an electrical charge
exists is the fundamental hypothesis on which the electrical
function of sexuality is based: however, what sexuality really
is, is not yet understood.

In general, the basic biological manifestation of sexuality
is motor activity accompanied by the rhythmic friction of two
excited body surfaces rubbing against each other. We know
also, through direct experience, that this is associated with
a subjective feeling of pleasure. But, until now, the objective
component of this friction-induced sensuality has not been
known. To confirm the electrical theory of sexuality, we must
readily demonstrate that both phenomena (objective and subjective) have as their common denominator changes in electrical
potential occurring at the pleasure site. The simplest form in
which sexual pleasure is felt is the sensation of itching or tickling. These cause an automatic release of the impulse to scratch
or to rub, and these actions seem to have a basic similarity
to sexual friction. These phenomena seem to be generally present among metazoal organisms.

From clinical data, we know that a feeling of pleasure cannot
be "commanded" into existence; the harder the mind tries
to induce it, the less likely it is to appear. This is especially
true when one tries to observe it in an experimental situation.
Electrophoto 7 shows the stimulation of a male tongue—first
by a resting electrode; then by gentle friction with the electrode;
and, finally, by thrice-repeated pressure with the electrode.

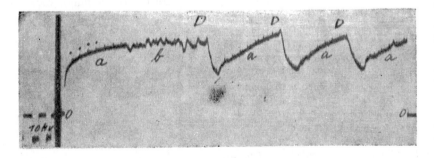

7. Mucous membrane of the tongue:
a=wandering; b=tickling; D=pressure

The experimental setup is as follows: the ground electrode is placed on the left foot, while the grid electrode is placed without pressure on the tongue. We note that when the circuit is closed a ground potential of about +20 mV appears, which in the course of about twelve seconds rises another 10–12 mV. As the tongue is gently stroked with the electrode, there is a further slow rise in the ground potential. We then see fluctuations of potential on either side of the ground-potential line, sometimes symmetrical, sometimes in a more or less positive or negative direction.[3]

This "tickling effect" can be demonstrated on any area of the body surface. However, repeated control experiments have failed to elicit it when the electrode is rubbed against inorganic substances (see below.) We will return later to the significance of this "tickling effect." On the tracing, one may observe that the positive (rising) arm of the oscillating deflection is generally steep, while the negative (downward) deflection is shorter and more gradual. This will be shown to be of some significance later. The EKG follows exactly all the fluctuations in potential. At "D," the electrode is pressed gently but firmly into the tissues of the tongue. The result is an immediate drop in potential of about 15–20 mV which returns slowly up to the previous level when the pressure is released. We also note that as the potential returns to its former level, it directly continues to follow the original "wandering" despite the interruption. This was regularly shown when the pressure was repeated on three additional trials. The pressure reaction also occurs on nonsexual areas, but without the wandering effect.

Electrophoto 8 shows the tickle reaction elicited by the KCl electrode on the inner surface of a girl's lower lip. The negative deflection during tickling comes from an unintentionally heavy pressure on the electrode; the sudden rise at "K" coincides with the beginning of a strong itching sensation. When the tickling stimulus is withdrawn, the potential drops somewhat, and the wandering in a positive direction gradually resumes.

The degree of rise in potential of the tickling effect is related: 1) inversely to the intensity of the pressure: the gentler the tickling, the steeper the rise; 2) directly to the excitability of the site; and 3) directly to the state of psychic readiness.

However, we cannot quantify this relationship until we can measure the *intensity* of the sensation. Yet everything seems

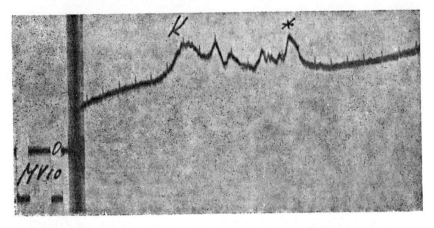

8. Mucous membrane of the lips: K to *=tickle phenomenon

to indicate that the rate of change in potential gives us the very yardstick we are seeking. As far as we can determine, the potential variations generated at or near ground level are not related to organ excitability or subjective mood and can be elicited at any time. However, we have never seen a steep rise in ground potential that was not accompanied by a simultaneous sensation of itching. Electrophoto 9 shows just how great the sudden jump in potential can be when the subject is in a suitably receptive mood.

The charge on the palmar surface yields a resting potential of about +20 mV. At the first tickling stimulus, it suddenly rises to about +55 mV. It then falls, apparently as a result of heavy pressure, to +10 mV, and climbs to +70 mV when the stimulus is repeated a second time. One may clearly see how the ground potential (along with the EKG complex) quickly builds up with each successive stimulation. We must, therefore, draw a careful distinction between: (1) the rise in the ground potential; and (2) the frictional fluctuations at or near ground potential level.

Electrophoto 10 shows the electrical charge on the same palmar surface after a two-minute rest. The ground potential starts off here at a level of +60 mV, compared to +20 mV

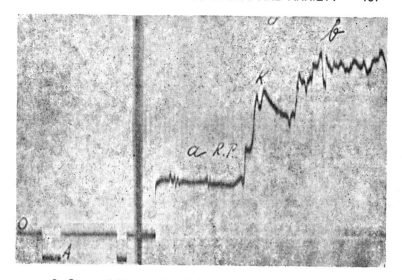

9. Strong tickle reaction of the palm: a=resting potential; k=tickling reaction

10. Same palm one minute later: D=pressure

obtained previously; it slowly begins to "wander"; then jumps to +85 mV when the tickling stimulus is applied; it then continues wandering up to +95 mV, while showing significant deflections due to the friction effect. When the tickling stimulus is removed, the tracing sinks slowly for 5mV over a period of about twelve seconds; thrice-repeated pressure with the electrode increases the negative drop by about 25 mV. A line drawn to join the points where the ground potential reappears after letup of pressure will represent the direct continuation of the ground potential's gradual fall.

From observations and control experiments, we maintain that inorganic substances show no such regularity and lawfulness in the process of acquiring electrical charge, and that these are properties specific to the organic world. We will return later to the implications of these facts in connection with other experiments.

We have now established the following facts:

1. *Tickling stimuli which elicit a pleasure or itching sensation increase the electrical surface charge.*

2. *Pressure stimuli regularly decrease the surface charge.*

Does this lawfulness have a universal significance?

The same female subject, retested in a neutral frame of mind, shows about the same amount of charge on the left and right palms, that is, a symmetry of charge. In both cases and in the controls, the ground potential is almost still. Wandering is minimal (Photos 11 and 12). Careful evaluation of the control data amassed leads to the following conclusion: *in a given*

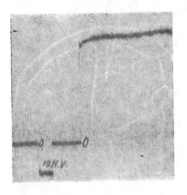 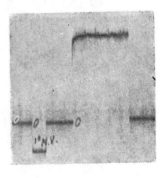

11. and 12. Symmetrical resting potentials of right and left palms

sexual organ, the capacity for excitation and the quantity of electrical charge can vary greatly from one time to another.

Tickling near the Electrode

In evaluating the tickling effect, we had to consider the following objection: were the results simply an expression of the potential gradient between the friction material and the skin? We therefore produced the tickle phenomenon in the following way: the electrode rested motionless on the skin site to be tested, while the skin area *adjacent* to the electrode was gently stroked with a dry cotton pledget or feather (both nonconductors). Again, the tickling effect appeared, just as it did when the electrode itself was used as a stimulus (Electrophoto 13).

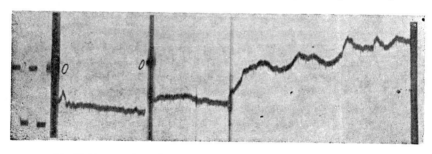

13. Tickle reaction of palm: tickling adjacent to resting electrode

In order to verify the functional identity of *objective* variations in potential and *subjective* sensations of tickling, the following experiment was performed.

A control subject observes the apparatus [in one room]; the experimental subject is placed in an adjoining room and connected to the recorder by a long cord. The subject, who must be capable of observing his feelings, is then told to indicate whether the tracing wanders or stays steady; whether the potential is rising or falling, etc. He is to do this, not on the basis of tactile sensation—but *according to the amount of tickling he feels.* The greater the subject's accuracy in observing his feelings, and the gentler the tickling (that is, the less contact there is between the tickling instrument and the skin), the more exact the results. We observed that quantitatively the objectively visible potential deflections reproduced—with photographic accuracy—the *intensity* of the [subjectively] felt pleasure experience. This was even more accurately reproduced when the intensity of the pleasure *currents* (*streaming*) was considered.

The experiment can also be performed in reverse by having one person indicate the reading of the tracing while the subject compares it to his own pleasure feeling. Naturally, this is not so satisfactory a method as the first.

14. Pleasure response (* to *) of an excited nipple

Electrophoto 14 gives the results of such an experiment. We observe the nipple potential of a female breast during the course of one minute. The grid electrode rests on the nipple while the subject tickles the nearby aureole with a pledget of dry cotton. The asterisk indicates the start of the tickling. Up to this point, we see a horizontal resting potential of about +20 mV. As soon as the tickling begins, it suddenly jumps higher and then slowly increases until just before the end, when it again rises rapidly to about +45 mV. Then, as the tickling stops, it falls again. The subject reported that she twice felt a strong sensation of pleasure "right at the beginning and toward the end." At the latter time, she even reported the fantasy of a child sucking her breast. She was, of course, unaware of what the tracing registered, and when shown a photograph of it exclaimed, "That's the God's truth all right!"

Since the quantity of the potential (objective parameter) corresponds to the intensity of the pleasure [subjective parameter], we may draw the following conclusion: *the vegetative pleasure currents are photographically reproduced by the variations in electrical charge on the erogenous skin surface.* The details of this will be discussed later.

(The thickness of the light-streak tracing is due to interference transmitted by the house current, which was not filtered out in this experiment.)

In this type of experiment, we must emphazise that the testing and reporting of sensations by the subject has a distracting influence on the subject's attention, and, therefore, tends to inhibit the development of vegetative streaming. Because of this, we would expect that in a spontaneous and undisturbed situation the intensity of sexual streaming would be significantly greater.

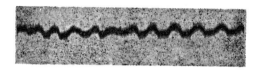

15. Reaction of penis to regular friction

The same experiment was conducted with the electrode placed on the penis; the results were the same. A regular friction stimulus applied near the electrode produces regular waves on the tracing (Photo 15). In this run, the apparatus was set at its lowest range of sensitivity (1/10). The deflections are in the 15-20 mV range.

In no case was a rise in potential observed when there was no feeling of pleasure associated with the stimulus. An indispensible requirement for conducting this experiment is the subject's ability to distinguish between a streaming sensation of pleasure and simple tactile or thermal sensation.

Anxiety and Unpleasure

In reviewing the literature on psychogalvanic skin reaction, I could find no statement as to any distinction between pleasure and unpleasure or anxiety phenomena. Physiologists who were consulted stated that no distinction could be made and that an increased negative charge would always result. But my concept of the antithesis of pleasure and anxiety, based on clinical observations, threw doubt on this. If psychic excitation is functionally identical to fluctuations in autonomic excitation, and the latter are observable as waves of electrical potential, then their view is untenable. Since the sensations of pleasure and anxiety are antithetical to each other (though identical *in origin*), this opposition should also apply to the direction of their electrical flow. The difficulty is that up to now, so far as I know, no one in the field of nerve and skin physiology has distinguished the *direction* of electrical flow resulting from excitation of an organ. Therefore this had to be worked out in the course of the present experiments.

Thus far we have quantified the various skin potentials as per their relationship to the grid potential, which is arbitrarily set at zero. We have also compared the potentials of various skin zones to each other. These differences are relative, since both sets of potentials are variable. We must now delineate more accurately a third aspect of electrical functioning.

The Direction of Change in Potential

So far we have called a potential positive or negative in relation to its value above or below the arbitrarily chosen zero level of the grid potential (e.g., $+15$ mV or -40 mV means 15 mV over or 40mV under the zero potential, respectively). One may further distinguish the *direction* of change in potential, and speak of a "rising" or "falling" potential; these may be read directly from the milliammeter of the apparatus.

We must keep clearly in mind that any rise in potential indicates an increase in positive potential, regardless of whether this occurs above or below the arbitrary zero line; the same applies to a fall or increase in negative potential. Let us stop considering the absolute or relative difference of the changes in potential, but observe only their direction of change. For example, a change from -40 to -20 mV would still be considered a positive change; likewise, a change from $+5$ to $+30$, or from -10 to $+10$ mV. Similarly, any change on the milliammeter from a higher to a lower figure is considered a negative change, and will show on the tracing as a movement from left to right, or on the photo of the tracing, as a movement from above to below.

*Lowering of the Surface Potential during
Anxiety and Unpleasure*

At the risk of repetition, we recall so far that stimuli that result in a streaming sensation of pleasure *increase* the electrical charge on the body surface. This is expressed as a rise in potential, that is, as a positive change in the grid potential. The light tracing is deflected to the left, the milliammeter registers an increased current flow, and the photo of the tracing shows an upward deflection.

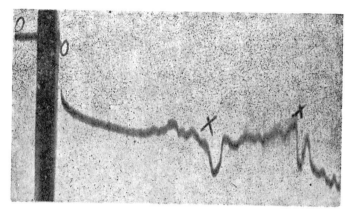

16. X=reaction of vaginal mucous membrane to a
stimulus of annoyance

Electrophoto 16 shows the change in potential accompanying a feeling of *annoyance*. The charge is measured at the vaginal introitus of a female hysteric (the same subject whose anal potential was measured previously). The vaginal measurement was done the same day as that of the premenstrual anal mucosa (cf. Photo 6).

The ground potential starts off at about −15 mV and quickly sinks to −25 mV. We will recall that the subject felt depressed and found the procedure quite disagreeable. She was isolated in a nearby room and was attached to the apparatus by a long cord. The ground electrode was attached to the leg and, like the grid electrode, was of KCl. The subject was asked simply to place the electrode on the labia majora. We noted a gradual decrease in potential, and then, suddenly, a steep negative deflection; at the same moment we heard a loud cry of annoyance from the adjoining room: a drop of KCl had fallen on the sensitive mucosal surface and irritated it. This point is marked by an "X" on the photo.

At the point indicated by the second "X," the subject became irritated once again and the potential dropped sharply about 20 mV.

A feeling of annoyance is accompanied by a decrease in electrical charge of the erogenous zones. Why does sexual excitability so quickly disappear in a state of irritation? When one is irritated, bioelectric excitation runs in a direction opposite to that of the sexual excitation: *therefore a decrease in surface charge occurs instead of an increase.*

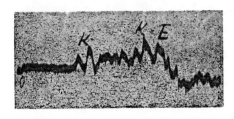

17. Tongue:
     K=tickle; E=fright

Photo 17 shows a similar occurrence on the tongue of a male subject. The ground potential starts quietly at about +2 mV; at K, tickling with the electrode begins; the ground potential rises gradually; at E, a sudden loud cry is made to frighten the subject; the potential drops about 20 mV; a repeated shout results in another potential drop, much less than before (not shown in this photograph). A third cry has no further effect. We note that the tickling effect, as well as the electrocardiogram, conforms to the drop in potential.

Before seeing the actual tracing, the subject, a psychology student, drew us a graph depicting his tongue sensations. His diagram bears an amazing likeness to the curve of the ground potential. Only the effects of the tickling stimulus are missing.

From clinical work in sex economy, we are familiar with an interesting subjective phenomenon: patients occasionally report that when frightened they feel something like an electric shock on the tongue. A patient reported a similar sensation when he suddenly discovered that his wife had been unfaithful.

In a state of anxiety or fright, there is a concomitant drop in electrical charge of the body surface. This is more pronounced at sexual zones than on the rest of the skin. A flaccid penis, which typically accompanies anger or anxiety, regularly shows a lowering of potential.

It is easier to obtain an anxiety reaction than a feeling of pleasure. We use an exploding paper bag or a sudden loud striking of a gong. On one occasion, the electrical response did not occur. The subject reported that the stimulus had caused an instantaneous feeling of *rage*. This raises the problem: what is the relationship between rage and the negative potential change produced by annoyance and anxiety?

In the above, we have some experimental support for the sex-economic concept of the biological *antithesis of pleasure and anxiety*: they are oppositely directed electrical currents. *During pleasure, the surface of the organism becomes more positively charged with respect to the interior; during displeasure, irritation, or anxiety, it becomes more negatively charged.*

Now that we have demonstrated the functional identity of pleasure, with a peripherally directed current flow, and of anxiety, with a centrally directed current flow, we still have an important objection to consider—namely, the appearance of the so-called cold erection or pleasureless erection of the penis. Experiments show that mechanical hyperemia is not sufficient to cause a feeling of pleasure: compression of the penile root and consequent blood congestion does *not* cause a change in potential. In addition to blood flow, something else must occur for excitation to result. The "streaming" quality felt during pleasurable erection is due to *mechanical hyperemia plus the electrical charging of the surface*: pleasure currents are felt only when there is a rise in the electrical potential. We draw a further conclusion from this: namely, that the biopsychic tendency "toward the world" and its opposite "away from the world," "withdrawal into the self," have an objective functional basis in the antithetical directions of streaming of the bodily electrical charges. *It is as if the living organism reaches out toward the world by charging its surface electrically. The charging of the periphery during pleasure excitation would seem to have the same functions as pseudopod extension in an amoeba or feeler extrusion in a snail.* Similarly, *the discharge of the periphery, and concomitant decrease in potential, would be the direct expression of a creeping back into the self.* This problem should certainly be explored further in animal experimentation.

The Basic Antithesis of Vegetative Life Functions

The Sugar-Salt Experiment. In the tickling experiment we were able to elicit streaming sensations of pleasure; however, we are not entirely clear about them since we cannot specify their range of intensity, that is, quantify the capacity to accept electrical charge. Clinical experience has shown that the surface of an organism is not charged artificially from without but biologically from within, from the "vegetative center," so to speak. This reaction requires the elimination of all inhibitions and external disturbances. In all previous experiments, we allowed pleasure feelings to be artificially "pumped up," so that they did not stream spontaneously. As a result, the excitation always acted like a cautious snail afraid to venture out of its shell. In order to achieve a spontaneous reaction, we conducted the following experiment with several subjects.

The cathode is placed in a vessel filled with normal saline. The grid electrode is wrapped in a saline-soaked cotton pad. One end of this long pad is placed in a dish containing concentrated sugar solution. The other end of the pad is thoroughly moistened with a solution of either sugar or salt. The subject then sucks on this end of the pad while placing a finger in the vessel containing the cathode, in order to complete the circuit. The technical correctness of this arrangement will be considered later.

We begin by giving sugar, without her knowledge, to a female subject known from her therapy to have a strong oral-erotic tendency. The first part of Electrophoto 18 shows no curve, since the tracing is too far to the left, that is, so far in a positive direction that it is out of the field. In the second part, a certain amount of adaptation has obviously occurred. In the third part, we see a curve rising in a positive direction, which clearly reproduces the sucking movements; it is analogous to the tracing produced by friction, with a steep rise followed by a more gradual falling off, and an increase in ground potential. In the

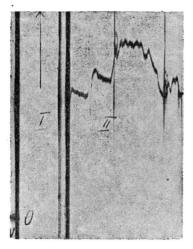

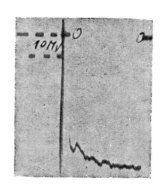

19. Reaction of
same tongue to salt

18. Reaction of tongue to sugar

second part, the zero line is displaced to the right, that is, toward the negative, for the sake of accuracy. The curve begins at a minimum of +70 mV and rises approximately another 20 mV. In a second subject (male), with no particular oral-erotic tendency, there was an initial rise of +mV[4] followed by an increase of 30 mV.

When we repeat the same experiment, using a concentrated salt solution, we obtain a diametrically opposite result, even to the form of the tracing itself: the ground potential starts at about −55 mV, does not vary up and down as in the sugar experiment, but plunges downward in an almost constant drop (Electrophoto 19).

If we apply salt to the mouth unexpectedly, we see a large negative deflection toward the right margin, in the opposite direction to that occurring when sugar was used.

The oral excitation quickly leaps out toward a pleasurable stimulus and pulls back from an unpleasant one. Thus the opposition between pleasure and unpleasure can be experimentally demonstrated and photographed. It is an objective fact, independent of any preconceived notions. The basic antithesis of vegetative life functions is manifested by pleasure, the peripherally directed flow of electricity, and by anxiety or unpleasure, the centrally directed flow.

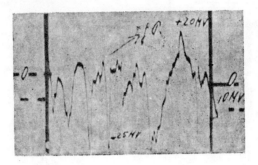

20. Reaction of tongue to sugar

The Form of the Excitation. So far we have considered only the height and direction of the excitation curve. But in comparing the sugar and salt reactions, one is struck by still another difference. The excitation curve of sugar is very "lively." In Electrophoto 20, we can clearly see the following: an increase in the positive deflections, that is, the most outwardly directed, toward-the-world strivings; but, in addition, we see strong negative deflections, which in turn give way to even stronger positive ones—deep clefts followed by steeply rising peaks. A very similar picture results when honey is sucked: each increase of excitation precedes a retreat. The reaction to salt, on the other hand, lacks this effect. Here (Electrophoto 21) we find a more or less regular "quiet" drawing back, once the first steep plunge of the ground potential has occurred. With different subjects, even the minor 2–3 mV fluctuations seen here are lacking: the excitation drops off uniformly.

The "Disappointment" Reaction. When one administers sugar first and then salt, the reactions follow the pattern described above, though in varying degrees. We may also note an habituation effect with repeated administrations of a sugar-salt sequence. With each successive run, the reaction to sugar shows a progressively lower potential. Likewise, the reaction to salt is not so intense as in the first trial, when the stimulus is unexpected.

On the other hand, if the salt is applied before the sugar, the reaction is completely negative, and the subsequent administration of sugar does not induce a rise in potential; the sugar actually results in a steep drop in potential.

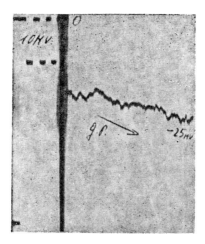

21. Reaction of same tongue to salt

This finding clearly indicates the biological nature of these reactions. Once the salt has been applied, the tongue behaves as if it had become cautious and refuses to be tempted; it reacts with anxiety even when sugar is given. On repeated trials, we find that [after "disappointment"], the tongue does not respond to sugar with an increase in charge until one-half to one hour later. Even so, we do not get the steep jump in charge seen on the first application of sugar, nor do we see the "lively" behavior shown in Electrophoto 21. The friction potential, normally seen with sucking, shows only small deflections and appears rather "sluggish."

In dealing with phenomena of electrical excitation, one may discern not only *quantity* and *direction* of flow, but varying degrees of *liveliness,* as well. The same organ may respond to a given stimulus in a quick and lively fashion at one time, and in a slow or sluggish manner at another, depending on its "mood." From this, we may draw the following conclusions:

1. The electrial response of a sexual organ depends not so much on the stimulus as on the state of readiness of the organism as a whole.

2. A "disappointed" organ reacts slowly and "cautiously."

3. When *habituation* to a given stimulus occurs, there is a reduction in the range of potential change, both positively

and negatively; that is, upward or downward deflections occur closer to the zero line.

We thus have experimental confirmation of some well-known aspects of sexual activity.

The response to a sexual partner is not always—indeed only rarely—contingent upon the amount of stimulation offered. Rather, it depends almost entirely on the individual's state of sexual readiness.

Also, during sexual activity, the genitals may experience a disappointment reaction, such as described above. A state of sexual arousal may be difficult or impossible to obtain. Instead of erection or vaginal secretions, flaccidity, dryness, even vaginismus, may ensue in the wake of severe genital anxiety, unpleasant circumstances, or painful associations. The genital is totally dominated by the impulse to withdraw; the opposite reaction, of erection, of "reaching out to the world," cannot occur. Thus, in cases of impotence or frigidity, the important consideration is not so much whether there has been a sexual threat at one time, but rather whether at that particular time the organ responded with a negative biological anxiety reaction which subsequently became fixed. For the subjective experience of genital anxiety to have a lasting effect, it must be structurally anchored in the form of a [conditioned] negative electrical response. In contrast to this is *pleasure anxiety*, which I shall discuss later.

Hypotheses Concerning the Pleasure Response. Control experiments on the above are feasible only if one becomes familiar with the peculiarly "cautious" quality of the peripheral electrical charge. The charge will not "venture out" in the presence of a third party, in the face of possible disturbance, or if the attention is not completely directed away from the outside world. We therefore need a series of complex setups to ensure valid results.

In charging the periphery to capacity, the decisive factor seems to be not the rise in potential itself, but the amount and extent of the deflections involved. The tracings of the sugar reaction show a rise in potential broken by deep clefts, corresponding to strong withdrawals of charge. From clinical data, we know that the greater the waves of excitation produced by coital friction movement, the greater the pleasure obtained. If the excitation mounts in a steady rise [rather than in peaks and clefts], the sex act will not be as pleasurable, even if the same potential height is eventually reached. It seems to depend upon the alternation of quiescence and activity, on the step-wise buildup of charge to the maximum charging capacity.

The tracings of the tickling response show alternate up and down movements corresponding to an increase and decrease of charge, respectively; we cannot properly call this decrease a "discharge." In the sugar response, the excitation on the tongue behaves like a suckling calf, which pulls away from the udder only to press forward again with increasing eagerness. It seems probable that each new movement leads to a fresh wave of pleasure. One thinks instinctively of a tiger or cat crouching before a leap—*contraction before maximum extension*. In this case, the state of contraction is not associated with any relaxation, but expresses a state of extreme inner tension. Since the charging of the periphery also reflects a directly observable state of tension, we must conclude that there are two different kinds of tension involved. Just before springing, there is a state of *central* tension in the organism; the greater this tension, the greater the motor impulse at the periphery. The withdrawal of charge from the periphery must necessarily lead to an increase of tension centrally. *Thus the electrical excitation springs, so to speak, from the center to the periphery.* This state of central tension can be directly perceived if during coitus one happens to stop a particularly pleasurable friction movement and lies perfectly still: one immediately feels a strong inner urge to resume the friction movement, that is, to build up the peripheral charge. We will consider this to-and-fro movement of the excitation in more detail later.

Therefore, we must carefully distinguish *four different types of negative electrical response at the periphery*:

1. Central tension stemming from charging of the periphery.
2. Peripheral orgastic discharge.
3. Anxiety reaction.
4. Extinction of the source of charge: death.

In all four cases, there is a reduction of the surface charge: the first is in order to recharge to a higher level—pleasure; in the second, all excitation above the resting potential is discharged to the outside—orgastic discharge; in the third, the tension remains fixed centrally—anxiety; the fourth corresponds to death. According to previous experimental results, dying tissues become increasingly negative as the central source of charge is extinguished.

By sorting out the various functions having the same direction of electrical excitation, we can better organize our wealth of data.

Electrical Excitation during Kissing

The Inadequacy of Direct Leads. From the very beginning of our investigations, we felt that a photographic tracing of electrical excitation in coitus would be an experimental goal of prime importance. However, our initial experimental setup, using direct leads from the test sites, made attainment of this goal seem unlikely. It is impossible to use direct leads for measuring the charge at the genitals during coitus. The manipulation alone would inhibit any excitation. Also, a direct lead is not entirely free from mechanical instability, which can give rise to unsteadiness and irregular, even broken, contacts. Finally, there is another difficulty to be overcome: namely, to rule out possible mechanical artifacts of the electrode itself. This is necessary even though the controls showed no deflections resulted from rubbing the electrode (or its rubber-sheathed tips) against glass or a cloth soaked in electrolytes. At first, there seemed no way out, as I labored under the misconception that the excitation could be tested only by direct leads. It was at this stage of the experiment that we took the following tracing of an ejaculatory excitation curve (Electrophoto 22).

The subject was orgastically disturbed. The act of masturbation was interrupted just before the ejaculation. The electrode (KCl) rested on the glans penis throughout the ejaculation. At the beginning of the climax, we see a positive rise in the ground potential. It continues to climb evenly, with steep rises in potential of about 10 mV. It is difficult to judge what relation the second major rise in positive potential, shown by the two peaks on the tracing, has to the first three sharp deflections due to the ejaculation. Since 2.3 mm. of tracing equals 1 second of time (accurately shown by the EKG complex), it appears that only the triple-peaked deflection corresponds to the ejaculation, while the other group reflects the postejaculatory penile spasms. The regularity of the intervals, and also the approximate height of the deflections (somewhat less than usual),

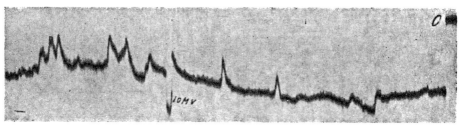

22. Orgastic excitation during masturbation

attest to the biological nature of the phenomena. In addition, there is the falling off of the ground potential after its initial rise.

Of course, there are uncertainties due to technical difficulties and the unusual emotional demands made on the subject; but there is no doubt about the basic features of the phenomenon. The form of the electrical excitation, the rise and fall in potential, accords with what was expected from clinical experience. In principle (regardless of the potential height), *the orgastic excitation curve must ascend and descend in equal amounts*; the steepness of the ascending portion is not seen here. After successful ejaculation, the ground potential remains steady (horizontal, in the photo) at about 25 mV. We should note that the curve of orgastic excitation, at least in this case, lacks the deep negative deflections seen in the preorgastic friction tracing. It is confined to the region *above* the ground potential, for example, on the positive side of the base line.

The Technique of Indirect Leads. In order to achieve our major goal [of recording the coital excitation curve], while sparing our subjects' feelings as much as possible, we had to consider the feasibility of using indirect leads. This raised the following question: if we attached the leads to a fingertip of each subject, could we separately measure the potential of two body surfaces in rhythmic friction with one another? This would give correct results only if: 1) the potential tracing obtained reproduced the form of the excitation coming from the test sites; 2) the attachment sites of the leads (the fingertips) did not move; 3) the ground potential of the two contiguous skin surfaces remained the same, regardless of the surface area in contact.

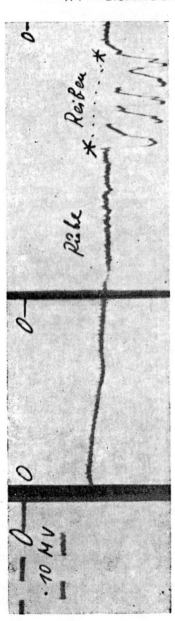

23. Contact potential of two fingertips

24. Rubbing of same fingertips on glass surface.

25. Stroking of palm

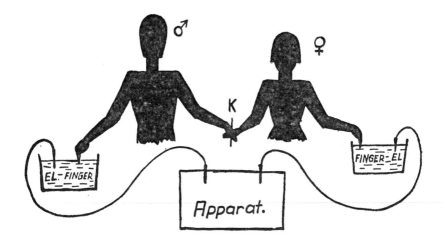

The following three electrophotos show tracings taken of:

1. The resting potential of two fingertips rubbing against each other (Electrophoto 23).

2. The pressure effect obtained by pressing a fingertip against the glass bottom of a vessel (Electrophoto 24).

3. The rise in potential resulting from the gentle, mutual, handstroking of two subjects (Electrophoto 25).

The experimental setup was as follows:

In the first photo, the EKGs of *both* subjects are superimposed on the tracing. The resting potential, as expected, starts off at about −20 mV. During the quiet interval [between the tests], the ground potential remains horizontal. The second photo shows several negative deflections, resulting from the heavy rubbing of a fingertip on the glass bottom of the electrolyte container. The third photo shows strong positive deflections, up to 20 mV—in other words, a 40 mV rise above the resting potential, resulting from gentle stroking. Direct observation showed that harsher pressure transformed the positive into a negative deflection—that is, it caused a fall in potential.

When the stroking stops, the ground potential returns to the resting state and a slow drop to the original resting potential is seen.

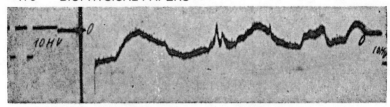

26. Hand stroking alternating with pressure

Electrophoto 26 shows, in unique fashion, the antithesis of *pleasure* and *pressure*: two hands are alternately pressed together and stroked in sequence. The results are checked by direct observation: every single rise in potential corresponds exactly to a pleasant feeling [of being stroked]; every fall occurs during heavy pressure. The ground potential shows a slight rise, on the whole. Two female subjects were used.

The results of this experiment recall the clinical observation that during the sex act, gentle friction heightens pleasure, while harsh friction decreases it.

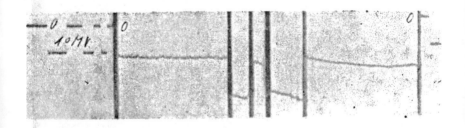

27. Contact potential of various skin areas

The following are the controls for our key experiment. Electrophoto 27 shows the respective potentials due to friction between:

1. Two fingertips, about −10 mV.
2. Two fingers, about −20 mV.
3. Two hands, about −10 mV.
4. Dorsal aspects of two forearms, about −20 mV.
5. Ventral aspects of two forearms, about −20 mV.

Encouraged by these irrefutable results, I photographed a pleasurable kiss between two individuals (Electrophoto 28).

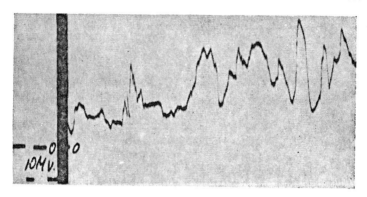

28. Excitation in kissing

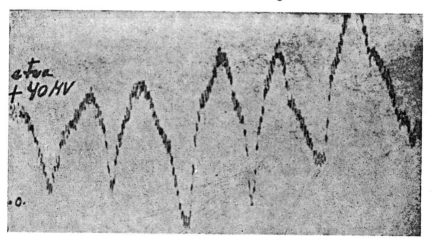

29. Kiss

We see the familiar effect of frictional excitation: steep peaks alternating with deep clefts.

Electrophoto 29 shows, "in slow motion," a greatly enlarged tracing of the frictional excitation. One centimeter on the horizontal axis corresponds to one second; one centimeter on the vertical axis equals about 3.3 mV.

The ground potential shows a rise, on the whole. We see that the various peaks of excitation show a basic similarity of form. However, the details are still to be worked out.

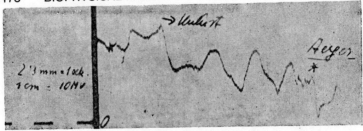

30. Unpleasurable kiss (*annoyance)

Electrophoto 30 shows the course of excitation during an unpleasant kiss with the same couple. The female partner shows visible malaise: the ground potential falls, and, at the same time, the frictional deflections grow smaller. At the end, a deep negative deflection is seen—sharp annoyance. This tracing was taken with rapidly moving film, as in slow-motion photography—one centimeter equals one second. The oscillations on the base line are artifacts of the oscillograph itself, as shown by the controls on inorganic substances.

From this we conclude: with minor exceptions, *the potential height shown by two quietly touching skin surfaces is independent of the surface area in contact,* provided that they are in an unexcited state.

On the basis of the foregoing experiments and controls, we used indirect leads to record the embrace of a naked couple, the male kissing the breast of the female (Electrophoto 31).

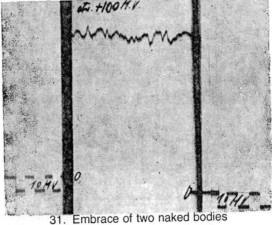

31. Embrace of two naked bodies

The ground potential registers a height of about 100 mV; the frictional deflections of the kiss amount to about 10 mV, as before. The two EKGs are visible. The bodies reposed quietly together. The complete excitation process was no doubt disturbed by the conditions of the experimental setup, but, in spite of that, a level of +100 mV was reached.

From this, we may rightly draw conclusions as to the maximum reachable potential of full sexual excitation during an undisturbed sex act. There is no longer any question of *whether* a process of electrical charge and discharge occurs in the sex act; rather, the problem is how to record such an excitation, in view of its strikingly high excursions above a photographic base line.

3. Results of Control Experiments

The electrical phenomena of the erogenous zones of the body would be far less meaningful if they did not specifically involve a process of biological excitation, that is, if the same phenomena were also to be shown by nonliving substances. On several occasions, I have alluded to control experiments on inorganic substances, which are summarized below:

1. *Sources of error due to inadequate insulation.*

Poorly insulated leads or electrodes may produce oscillographic deflections not originating in the skin sites being measured. For example, if the researcher or another individual collides with a subject connected to the apparatus, an immediate negative deflection is recorded. The degree of deflection varies with the person causing the movement. This source of error is easily spotted, since the previous potential level quickly reappears, and no such deflection shows up in the reruns. The condensor in the circuit was connected in such a way that any such source of error would produce a negative, rather than a positive, deflection.

Poorly insulated electrodes invariably gave negative deflections, thus indicating a current loss. The electrode leads had to be firmly fixed; mechanical movement of the wires would show up in irregular bursts on the oscillograph once the circuit was closed.

Unless a Faraday cage is used, the house current must be turned off or the apparatus is affected. The potentials are still measurable, but the tracing is not as sharp.

2. *Could the phenomena reported here be artifacts of purely local effects around the electrodes?*

For the *direct* leads, unpolarized electrodes of 0.1 N KCl solution were used.

The KCl electrodes were supplied by Doctors Hoffman and Lowenbach of the mental hospital at Dikemark. For the direct leads, a small rubber washer was attached to the skin, without pressure, and covered with a small watch glass, through which we fused a platinum wire coated with silver chloride. This served as the unpolarized electrode. When used properly, the electrodes gave readings of within half a millivolt of each other. We introduced the KCl solution through a small aperture in the watch glass, taking care, of course, to avoid the presence of air bubbles.

The electrodes used for measuring the hand potentials were insulated with rubber and glass and shielded with a metal casing. Rubbing the electrode against the bottom of a glass container or heating the KCl solution produced no deflection on the tracing. Likewise, touching the KCl electrodes to the leads at various points in the hookup produced no variations in charge.

For the indirect [ground] leads, we used pure silver electrodes. If we placed them in KCl solution and closed the circuit, a swift negative deflection of variable intensity resulted. However, no significant deflection appeared when we wrapped the ends of the electrodes in KCl-soaked wadding, placed them on two KCl-soaked cotton pads, and immersed them in the electrolyte container.

3. *Could variations in electrolyte concentration be a source of error?*

At first, we used only KCl electrodes. However, since these proved irritating to mucosal surfaces, we subsequently changed to 0.9 N saline solution. To rule out errors due to variations in the type or strength of solutions used, we repeatedly ran the following control experiments:

a. Silver electrodes wrapped in cotton soaked in 0.1 N KCl cause virtually no deflections, though exceptionally one gets a deflection of about −5 mV.

b. Similar results are obtained if cotton soaked in 0.9 N saline is wrapped around the silver electrodes.

c. If a more concentrated solution is used, the zero line remains unchanged.

d. With a more concentrated sugar solution, deflections of up to 10 mV may be observed.

e. If we pour concentrated saline solution on cotton soaked in 0.1 N KCl, deflections of between −5 and −10 mV appear.

If instead of directly immersing the electrodes, we connect them to various solutions through a cotton wick soaked in 0.9 saline, we get the following results:

NaCl (0.9 N)	no deflection
Concentrated NaCl	−5 to −8 mV deflections
Concentrated sugar solution	deflections up to −10 mV
Concentrated sugar mixed with concentrated salt solution	deflections up to −10 mV

The fact that variations in ionic concentration seem to play an insignificant role is probably due to the use of a two-megohm resistance in the circuit between the electrode and the amplifier tube. This allows virtually no flow of current and measures only the electric potential. Thus, the basic features of the sugar-salt experiment are not obscured by the effects of concentration, even if we disregard the unmistakable biological phenomena.

4. *Can the aforementioned effects of pressure, tickling, and stroking be reproduced in nonliving substances?*

If we connect two electrodes together by means of a towel soaked in KCl or saline solution, we get a negative deflection of about 20 to 40 mV on closing the circuit. However, no manipulation of the cloth with an *insulated* material can elicit any deflection. On the other hand, if a finger is rubbed on the cloth, the typical "wandering" effects, etc., are produced. Thus if someone were careful about the experimental results on living substances, but less careful with the controls, he might, for example, press the silver electrode into the cloth

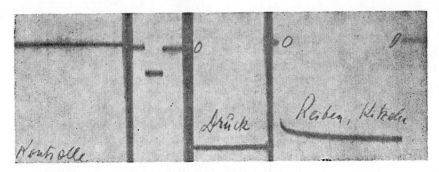

32. Control experiment with wet towel: pressure, rubbing, tickling

with his finger and jump to the conclusion that "even the towel is 'alive'" (Electrophoto 32).

If we increase the distance between the two electrodes on the cloth, the resistance is likewise increased, and the results remain negative.

In rechecking the experimental results, one can always easily disprove the findings simply by being careless. Thanks to one such "contradictory" experiment, a new problem arose, one for which we have not yet found a solution. We attached a catatonic subject to the apparatus and placed the differentiated [grid] electrode on the back of his hand. We then tickled it near the electrode with a piece of dry cotton and obtained the familiar "tickle effect." As a control, the cloth on which the hand lay was moistened with KCl solution, and we then tickled the cloth itself with the cotton—and obtained the same pattern of deflection! The problem seemed insoluble. Only on the following day did it strike me that during the control run the indifferent electrode had still been connected to the subject's leg. Thus a circuit of leg-body-hand-wet towel had been operating. This invalidated the control experiment. Furthermore, there still remained the important question of why the "tickle phenomenon" appeared, as though somehow the ability of living tissue to show this effect had been transferred to the electrolyte-soaked cloth. Meanwhile, the deflection caused by this "living cloth" remains unexplained.

5. With one exception, we were unable to elicit any potential rise in nonliving substances tested under the same circumstances. We must add, however, that this is true only in accor-

dance with the control experiments performed up to now.

If two closed electrical contacts are brought together, no deflection results; if they are placed in solution, the potential shows a steep and rapid drop.

Deflections can be produced by rubbing the electrodes on a metallic substance, but such results are negative in direction, not reproducible, and completely arrhythmic.

If the electrodes are rubbed on a flashlight, positive deflections result. However, one immediately recognizes that they lack the rhythmic quality of the "wandering" obtained with living substances (Electrophoto 33). The increases in potential are arrhythmic and have a mechanical, angular appearance. Since the surface of the flashlight is charged electrically from within, there is a certain similarity to what occurs in a living organism. However, the tracings produced are quite different in appearance.

These control experiments demonstrate that excitation phenomena cannot be produced in nonliving substance.

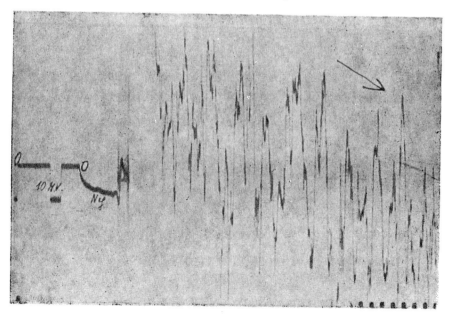

33. Control experiment with flashlight

6. It may be noted that the direction of the EKG varies up and down from one place to the next.

The direction of the cardiac complex is independent of the phenomena of sexual excitation. The potential rise caused by tickling is always the same (upward), regardless of whether the EKG points up or down. Controls show that the cardiac complex is positive when the left hand is connected to the cathode and the right to the grid. If the connections are reversed, the EKG points in the opposite direction. We cannot explain these findings at present, but they appear to be related to the polarity of the systolic electrical impulses. Undoubtedly, the potential variations reflect at the skin surface what is generated in the heart. Self-observation shows us that *each heartbeat is accompanied by a pulse of sensation* which we localize in the general cardiac region. This sensation is nothing but the onset of a feeling whose *fully developed* form we perceive as anxiety or pleasure. The details are still obscure.

7. If we connect the leads to a radio amplifier instead of the oscillograph, the potential variations will be transformed into sound instead of light.

The steady low hum of the amplifier disappears completely if the two electrodes are connected by electrolyte-soaked cotton; this corresponds to a negative deflection of the light tracing. With indirect leads connected to two touching palmar surfaces, a rhythmic sound results if they are rhythmically stroked together. Gentle stroking increases the intensity of the tone, while pressure decreases it. This corresponds completely to the light tracing on the oscillograph.

4. The Autonomic Center

Experimental investigation of skin potentials in pleasure and anxiety has supported our hypothesis that the process of excitation gives rise to two opposite directions of flow of bioelectrical current: toward the *periphery* and toward the *center*. The question of the nature of the current may now be clearly answered. The sensation of streaming is not solely contingent upon the blood flow in pleasure and anxiety, but also depends on the transmission of electrically charged particles by the blood and lymph streams. It has long been known that ionic currents exist in the blood. The skin now turns out to be the peripheral site at which the electrical charges are deposited or with-drawn—the autonomic periphery, so to speak. The existence of the direction "toward the world," on which we based our sex-economic theory of the instincts, is clearly confirmed.

However, the nature of the direction "away from the world, into the self " has remained less clear until now. Where is the bioelectric current concentrated during anxiety? This brings up the question of the autonomic center.

Where in the body are the sources and storage areas of bioelectrical energy to be found? Our first hypothesis was—*the autonomic nervous system (primarily the celiac, hypogastric, and pudendal plexuses).* I will shortly offer clinical support for this assumption. *The autonomic nervous system represents the generator, that is, the source, of the electrical energy of the human body.* The experimental investigations reported in the first part of this paper thoroughly substantiate this assumption. Now let us test to what extent it is supported by clinical facts, and how it enables us to comprehend hitherto unexplain-able phenomena in neurotic and emotional disorders.

To do this, we must free ourselves from a preconceived notion that conventional thinking in neurology and medicine tends to foster. The term "center" usually refers to the cere-brum and its associated relay stations through which the nerve impulses are conducted. It would be premature to discuss in detail the appropriateness of such a use of this term. In any case, it involves the mechanical concept of the cerebrum as the true control center and source of all impulses transmitted to the rest of the body. The cerebrum is seen as the ruler, so to speak, of all of man's actions. However, recent work in neuropathology (especially that of Goldstein) has sought to bring forth a completely new concept that would seem to deprive the cerebrum of its hitherto dominant function. The discovery of the autonomic functions has excited the interest of all branches of medicine. Moreover, the essential workings of this system and its relationship to the psyche are being eagerly explored.

My formulation of the function of the vagal and sympathetic

systems, the basic antithesis of vegetative life functions, is in complete accord with this newer direction and opposes on many counts mechanistic cerebral physiology. A lengthy discussion would be premature here, but we must make clear that the expression "autonomic center" implies much more than merely the "center" of the autonomic nervous system: it really connotes the center of all biophysiological and character-affective functioning in general. According to this view, the cerebrum—conservatively speaking—is only a specially developed accelerating and braking apparatus for the *totality of autonomic bodily functions*. This view is supported by the undeniable fact that the living organism shows an instinctive purposefulness long before the cerebrum is developed. In particular, the emotional processes, such as pleasure, anxiety, and anger, which have so greatly concerned us here, are by no means dependent on the existence of the cerebrum. Autonomic functions are phylogenetically older than those of the cerebrum. Thus the expression "autonomic center" has a much deeper significance than might appear at first glance. We must assume that cerebral functioning is also dependent upon autonomic functioning in general.

If we place a grid electrode on the epigastrium, about halfway between the umbilicus and the xiphoid process, the skin potential usually registers about −20 to −40 mV. If a finger is pressed into the abdomen near the electrode, there is a steady drop in potential of about 10 to 20 mV. *The same thing happens when the subject bears down as if at stool or inhales deeply.* One may object that the fall in potential is due to finger pressure on the skin. But, since deep inspiration produces the same kind of potential drop, this objection is invalid. When the subject exhales, the skin potential slowly rises to its previous level. During respiration, patients who are chronically held in the diaphragm and unable to exhale fully show lower and less clearly defined potential deflections than subjects with complete respiratory motility. This symptom warrants careful consideration. During inspiration, the diaphragm descends, compressing the organs beneath it; the abdominal cavity diminishes in volume, while the chest expands. During expiration, the opposite occurs: the chest contracts, and the abdomen expands. A second phenomenon points in the same direction. On deep inspiration, all vegetative streaming sensations subside completely in the upper abdomen. Conversely, on deep expiration, sensations akin to pleasure or anxiety appear in the upper abdomen or lower chest.

A glance at the organs of the abdominal cavity will clarify these experimental results. We see that two important organs lying beneath the dome of the diaphragm are mechanically displaced by the diaphragmatic movement. These are the stomach and the underlying *solar plexus*, the largest plexus of the autonomic nervous system. We have observed empirically that pressure reduces the buildup of electrical charge. We must further assume that the skin is continually being charged by a steady bioelectric current arising from a "still undetermined center." With pressure or anxiety, the charge on the skin decreases. In a state of pleasure, the bioelectrical charge reaches out like an animal to contact the outside world; in a state of anxiety, it pulls back. Now let us try to picture what happens to the viscera surrounding the abdominal and pelvic nerve plexuses when a person is in a state of fright:

1. The breath is drawn in deeply, and the shoulders are pulled up.
2. The abdominal muscles contract tightly.
3. The pelvic floor quickly pulls up.

Thus the abdomen behaves in anxiety like a creature that has something to protect. The walls press more closely on its contents. It seems obvious that what is being protected is the highly sensitive ganglia apparatus of the abdomen and the pelvis. The drop in abdominal skin potential upon compression or contraction of the abdominal wall can only be explained by the fact that an increased pressure is exerted on the plexus, which inhibits its bioelectrical activity. We will substantiate this theory in a later presentation of clinical data. Briefly stated: *it is now possible to understand neurotic sexual stasis, on a physiological basis, as the expression of the impaired functioning of the autonomic ganglia.*

5. Some Final Theoretical Conclusions

1. *Sexual excitation is functionally identical to the electrical charging of the erogenous zones.* The excitation during anxiety

is associated with diminution of charge on the surface of the body. The concept of "libido" as a measure of "psychic energy" no longer remains a metaphor, but refers to [measurable] electroenergetic phenomena. In this manner, the sexual function falls within the general category of natural electrical processes.

2. The skin and mucosal surfaces maintain a *"resting potential"* (RP) that varies within certain limits in the same individual and corresponds to a nonexcited state of the organism. The resting potential reflects a regular, continuous bioelectric charge on the surface of the organism.

3. The autonomic ganglia ("vegetative center"), together with the body's membrane-electrolyte biosystem, functions as the source of the electrical surface charge. The erogenous zones are endowed with a greater intensity of feeling and a higher charging capacity than other skin areas. In addition to greater excitability, they show a higher resting potential in general and a correspondingly greater range of oscillation when excited. Intense excitation, subjectively felt as mounting excitement or streaming sensations, corresponds to a state of higher electrical potential. Similarly, decreased excitation reflects a fall in potential. Specific feelings of pleasure or pain can be clearly differentiated from simple sensations of touch or pressure which are not associated with pleasure or pain. This accords with our clinical observation that states of sexual excitement or anxiety stand out clearly from any other kind of feeling both quantitatively and qualitatively. They can also be clearly differentiated from any other process by experimental means.

4. In its simplest form, pleasurable excitation manifests itself as a sensation of itching or tickling. The potential of an erogenous zone varies with the presence or absence of itching or tickling sensations. In the end stages of character analysis, some patients, for the first time, experience what they call "streaming," "sweet feelings," or "thrills"; these can be correctly understood as the preorgastic excitation or preorgastic rise in potential. The rise in preorgastic excitation is quantitatively identical to the upsurge of pleasure felt by the subject and to the soaring potential registered by the erogenous zone involved.

5. Passive mechanical congestion of a sexual organ will not cause any increase in charge over 'the resting potentia,. On the other hand, if the turgor and hyperemia are associated

with sex play and feelings of pleasure, a clearly visible potential rise appears above the RP level. In other words, mechanical tumescence must be accompanied by an electrical surface charge in order for a pleasurable, that is, a "sexual" feeling to result. The positive findings of this experiment support the assumption that the transition from mechanical congestion to electrical charge is a specifically sexual-biological process. The first part of the orgasm formula is confirmed.

6. Sexual friction is a biological function stemming from the *alternation of charge and discharge*. The discharging is always connected with pleasure; the charging, then, is always pleasurable if it is followed by discharge.

7. When excited, an emotionally healthy subject, who is capable of orgastic and preorgastic sensations, can accurately describe the oscillographic tracing purely on the basis of his subjective feelings. *The intensity of the pleasure feeling corresponds to the quantity of electrical surface charge, and vice versa.*

8. The success of these experiments is of great significance for the theory of the body-mind relationship. For we have confirmed the existence of an orgastic and preorgastic potential and shown that the accompanying sensations exactly mirror the objectively measurable process of electrical excitation. We have in this manner demonstrated the functional identity and antithesis of the somatic processes with the subjective pleasure-anxiety feelings. *The quantity of the surface potential and the intensity of the pleasurable or vegetative sensations are functionally identical.* There remains the deep question as to why nonerogenous sensations such as touch or pressure do not result in *any* potential rise.

9. Since only pleasurable vegetative sensations give rise to an increased surface charge, while pain, anxiety, annoyance, pressure, etc., cause it to fall, we must assume that pleasurable excitation is the *specific* process of all living organisms. Other biological processes show this also—for example, cell division, in which the cell shows an increase in surface charge coinciding with the biologically productive process of mitosis. Hence the sexual process would simply be the biologically productive energy process. Anxiety would be the antithetical basic biological tendency, which is akin to death but not identical to it.

10. If we assume that the orgasm is a fundamental manifesta-

tion of living matter, the orgasm formula of tension-charge-discharge-relaxation must represent *the general formula for all biological functions* and does not apply to nonliving processes. The heart, intestines, lungs, and bladder, as well as the single dividing cell, must, therefore, function according to this biological rhythm.

11. The economic regulation of sexual energy (that is, pleasure or electrical energy) and the sex-economic relationships between individuals now hold a new and deeper significance for the understanding of organ pathology and disease, which must be interpreted as disturbances of the autonomic equilibrium.

As we weigh this series of crucial and far-reaching conclusions, we must guard against the danger of playing theoretical games and letting them take the place of sound clinical fact-finding and basic experimental work. The reverse danger is of equal consequence—that is, failure to back up the empirical findings with correct hypotheses and the revision of deep-seated but meaningless preconceptions.

Notes

Foreword

[1]E. F. Baker, *Man in the Trap,* New York, Macmillan, 1967.

Translator's Preface

[1]Starting in the mid 1930s, with the work of H. S. Burr of Yale University, a growing body of classical research has emerged on the demonstration of a little-understood energy field around all living organisms. According to Burr (in a conversation with the writer), this empirically demonstrable field is neither electrostatic nor electromagnetic in nature. Contrary to other authors, he prefers the term "electrodynamic" and sees it as a basic attribute of all protoplasm. An excellent summary and extensive bibliography on the subject may be found in an article by L. J. Ravitz under the title "History, Measurement and Applicability of the Electromagnetic Field in Health and Disease," in *Annals of the New York Academy of Sciences,* Vol. 98, 1962.

The Impulsive Character

[1][First published in] 1923 [and in] *Ges. Schriften,* VI, Vienna, 1924–34.
[2]See "Zur Geschichte der psychoanalytischen Bewegung," [published] 1914, [and in] *Ges. Schriften,* IV, Vienna, 1924–34.
[3]In the interim, Abraham had published his highly informative *Psychoanalytische Studien zur Charakterbildung,* Internat. PsA. Bibl., XVI, 1924, in which he considers character analysis absolutely essential (see p. 64).
[4]"Entwicklungsziele der Psychoanalyse," *Neue Arb. z. ärztl. PsA.,* I, 1923.
[5]"Charakter und Analerotik," [published] 1908, [and in] *Ges. Schriften,* V, Vienna. 1924-34.

[6]"Beiträge zur Lehre vom analen Charakter," *Int. Ztschr. f. PsA.*, V, 1919.

[7]"Ergänzungen zur Lehre vom Analcharakter," *Int. Ztschr. f. PsA.*, IX, 1923, and a recently published monograph, p. 7.

[8]Freud, "Jenseits des Lustprinzips," [published] 1920, [and in] *Ges. Schriften*, VI, Vienna, 1925–34.

[9]Translation from Freud, Standard Ed., *The Ego and the Id and Other Works*, Vol. XIX, London, Hogarth Press, 1961, pp. 29-30.

[10]Translation from Freud, *ibid*, pp. 30-31.

[11]In "Drei Abhandlungen zur Sexualtheorie," *Ges. Schriften*, V, Vienna, 1925–34, p. 117, Freud observes: "It cannot be a matter of indifference whether a certain trend shows up before or after its countertrend... a chronological deviation in the synthesis of the components usually leads to a change in the end result." It is thus a question of finding typical deviations from the normal timetable of development and relating them to specific pathological results.

[12]"Kastrationskomplex und Charakter," *Int. Ztschr. f. PsA.*, VIII, 1922.

[13]"Über die Erziehung in Besserungsanstalten," *Imago*, 1923.

[14]Translation from Freud, *op. cit.*, p. 00.

[15]*Klinische Psychiatrie*, Leipzig, 1916.

[16]*Lehrbuch der Psychiatrie*, Leipzig, 1918.

[17]"Die Beurteilung psychopathischer Konstitution (sogenannter psychischer Minderwertigkeit)," *Ztschr. f. ärztl. Fortbildung*, IX, 1912.

[18]*Die psychopathischen Persönlichkeiten*, Vienna, 1923.

[19]"Die Psychosen bei psychopathisch Minderwertigen," *Allg. Ztschr. f. Psych.*, 1898.

[20]*Über psychopathische Persönlichkeiten*, Wiesbaden, 1909.

[21]"Über den Begriff d. psychopath. Konstitution," *Ztschr. f. ärztl. Fortbildung*, 1917.

[22]"Die abnorme Charakteranlage," *Arch. f. Krim. Anthr.*, 1912.

[23][The text literally reads, "the impulsivity of a neurotic personality. ..." It is obvious from the context that the author is referring to the impulsive character.—*Trans.*]

[24]I should like to express my deep gratitude to Professor Wagner-Jauregg for affording me the opportunity of studying the excellent clinical material.

[25]"Über Depersonalisation," *Internat. Ztschr. f. PsA.*, X, 1924.

[26]Kretschmer, E., *Der sensitive Beziehungswahn*, Berlin, 1918.

[27]*Körperbau und Charakter*.

[28]"Schizoidie und Syntonie," *Ztschr. f. ges. Psych. u. Neur.*, 1923.

[29]Reich, "Eine hysterische Psychose in statu nascendi," to be published soon in the *Int. Ztschr. f. PsA.* [Article subsequently appeared in Vol. XI, 1925 of the journal cited.—*Trans.*]

[30]"Das ökonomische Problem des Masochismus," *Int. Ztschr. f. PsA.*, 1924, [and in] *Ges. Schriften*, V.

[31]See especially Rank, *Das Trauma der Geburt*, Int. PsA. Bibl., XIV, 1924, and Garley's excellent article "Der Chok des Geborenwerdens," *Int. Ztschr. f. PsA.*, X, 1924.

[32]Once, in a private discussion, we raised the question as to whether such positive ego ideal demands exist at the very outset. We entertain the possibility that all "shall" enjoinders themselves evolve from prohibitions in complex ways.

[33]"Zur Genese des weiblichen Kastrationskomplexes," *Int. Ztschr f. PsA.*, IX, 1923.

[34]"Einige Bemerkungen zur Trieblehre," *Int. Ztschr. f. PsA.*, I, 1913.

[35]*Genitaltheorie*, Int. PsA. Bibl., XV, 1924.

[36]As Helene Deutsch informed me, she has reached the same conclusion by a different route, in her forthcoming *Psychoanalyse der weiblichen Sexualfunktionen*.

[37]*Das Wesen der Geschlechtlichkeit*, Jena, 1919.

[38]We add here the qualification that the attitude and reaction of the nurturer can reinforce erogenous tendencies.

[39]Thus a protracted period of nursing reinforces the oral position, while an anal-oriented milieu strengthens the anal position.

[40]*Geschlechtsverirrungen*, Vienna, 1921.

[41]Über eine besondere Form des neurotischen Widerstandes gegen die psychoanalytische Kur," *Int. Ztschr. f. PsA.*, VI, 1920.

[42]Reich, "Zwei narzisstische Typen," *Int. Ztschr. f. PsA.*, VIII, 1922.

[43]Abraham, "Entwicklungsgeschichte der Libido," *Neue Arb. z. ärztl. PsA.*, No. II, 1924.

[44]A particular incipient form of this conflict is described by Freud in "Einem Falle weiblischer Homosexualität," *Int. Ztschr. f. PsA.*, 1920 [and in] *Ges. Schriften*, V: The girl turns away from the father and in womanhood seeks out a masculine woman. The special conditions which give rise to the conflict remain unknown. (Strong mother—weak father?)

[45]"Ein hysterisches Symptom bei einem zweieinvierteljahrigen Kinde," *Imago*, IX, 1923.

[46]"Entstehung des Beeinflussungsapparates in der Schizophrenie," *Int. Ztschr. f. PsA.*, V, 1919.

[47]"Über den katatonen Anfall," *Int. Ztschr. f. PsA.*, VI, 1920.

[48]"Formulierungen über zwei Prinzipien des psychischen Geschehens," *Ges. Schriften*, V, 1911.

[49]"Die Ambivalenz des Kindes," *Imago*, VI, 1924.

[50]"These crazy moods, to nature ascribed, though solely sown by nurture...." writes Rousseau in his *Confessions*.

[51]I should only like to call attention to the strange position of the "shelves." It is totally reminiscent of the development of the amniotic membrane. I am avoiding any attempt at interpretation but would like to point out that the patient, as far as we know, had never seen a picture of the embryonic set-up and that this fantasy had existed since early childhood.

[52]The fantasy of the dirt-filled vaginas.

[53]"Gruppe der Schizophrenien," in Aschaffenburg, *Handb. d. Psychiatrie*, 1911.

[54]*Klinische Psychiatrie.*

[55]*Psychopathologie*, Berlin, 1920.

[56]*Seele und Leben*, Berlin, 1923.

[57]"Ein Betrag zur Lehre von den reaktiven Psychosen," *Monatsschr. f. Psychiatrie u. Neur.* 57, 1924.

[58]*Körperbau und Charakter*, Berlin, 1922.

[59]The discussion of the etiology of schizophrenia has been well organized by Wilmann, who put the psychoanalytic viewpoint in proper perspective. ("Die Schizophrenie," *Ztschr. f. d. ges. Neur. u. Psych.*, 78, "Vortäge zur Schizophreniefrage.") Compiled here is all the pertinent literature.

All the cases of impulsives with strong asocial trends whom I studied analytically and observed personally had this in common: since early childhood,
their activities were unrestrained. Gerstmann and Kauders published some
interesting cases who, following an encephalitic illness, and, during a post-
encephalitic condition bordering on hyperkinesia, developed a dyssocial, impulsive state. (Über psychopathieähnliche Zustandsbilder bei Jugendlichen,"
Archiv f. Psychiatrie, 1924.) The analyst should not disregard such facts.
The cases cited were not, of course, fully examined with regard to their premor-
bid personality; in particular, the libidinal transformations are not discussed.
Therefore, further conclusions are not permissible. We would only like to
point out that Schilder and others have repeatedly discussed the problem
as to what extent brain disease triggers psychogenic processes. The fact that
a disease of the midbrain or basal ganglia "begets" a dyssocial reaction is
as incontrovertible as the fact that paresis "produces" delusions. Certainly
a somatic process can occasionally encroach upon psychic causality.
("Cortex—Stammganglien: Psyche—Neurose," *Ztschr. f. d. ges. Neur. u.
Psychiatrie,* 74, 1922, and "Über den Wirkungswert psychischer Erlebnisse
und über die Vielheit der Quellgebiete der psychischen Energie," *Arch. f.
Psych.,* 1923. Also, *"Seele und Leben,"* Berlin, 1923.)

⁶⁰"Psychologie des Misstrauens," *Imago,* VII, 1921.

⁶¹We allude here to an observation of Sachs in his "Zur Genese der Perver-
sionen," *Int. Ztschr. f. PsA.,* IX, 1923: "In the pervert, if repression is partly
successful it must opt for a compromise: it must allow the retention of pleasure
as part of the complex, so that the ego may incorporate it and sanction it,
so to speak..." It is an open question whether this sanctioning by the ego
or the pervert's avoidance of unpleasure implies an ego structure similar to
that of the impulsive.

⁶²Italics added.

⁶³Translation from Sigmund Freud, *The Ego and the Id,* translated by Joan
Riviere, revised and newly edited by James Strachey (New York: Norton,
1962), p. 41.

⁶⁴*Ibid.,* pp. 41–42 (italics added).

⁶⁵With regard to the unconscious acceptance of superego demands shown
by religious, ascetic compulsives, there is obviously a much deeper unconscious
basis for this.

⁶⁶This fact only appears to contradict what we observed in the second
chapter, namely, that the impulsive character shows repressions as intense
as those of the impulse-inhibited neurotic. This clinical fact is fully compatible
with the isolated position of the ego ideal in that it certainly hinders the latter's
efforts at repression but does not completely block them. Also, it is possible
that only a part of the ego ideal has undergone the vicissitudes of isolation.

⁶⁷Cf. "Entwicklungsstufen des Wirklichkeitssinnes," *Int. Ztsch. f. PsA.,*
I, 1913.

⁶⁸We do not forget that there are *direct* identifications in the ego. Whether
the basic identifications occur in the ego or ego ideal can be of decisive importance for the personality structure. (Cf. my discussion of faulty sexual identifications, Chapter 3.)

⁶⁹Cf. Chapter 3.

⁷⁰Cf. Reich, "Weitere Bemerkungen über die therapeutische Bedeutung der

Genitallibido," *Int. Ztschr. f. PsA.*, XI, 1925.

[71]Freud, "Psychoanalytische Bemerkungen über einen autobiographisch beschriebenen Fall von Paranoia," *Ges. Schriften*, VIII. See also Freud, "Über einige neurotische Mechanismen bei Eifersucht, Paranoia und Homosexualität," *Internat. Ztschr. f. PsA.*, VIII, 1922; *Ges. Schriften*, V.

[72]After I completed this manuscript, a paper by T. H. Van der Hoop appeared, entitled, "Über die Projektion und ihre Inhalte" (*Int. Ztschr. f. PsA.*, X, 1924). The author arrives at conclusions similar to mine by viewing the essential process of projection from a different angle (p. 288): "Psychologically speaking, schizophrenia should be regarded as an intense state of introversion, marked by an ever-increasing process of regression which follows an infantile archaic phase of development; in the latter, there is minimal or no differentiation between subject and object, and, for this reason, the process of projection can become manifest with an inordinately powerful influence." However, intense introversion is not an adequate explanation, because introversion itself is only a sequel of fixation at this phase.

[73]To avoid misinterpreting the expression "earliest identification," which we purposely chose, one must bear in mind that, like Freud, we distinguish between two phases of identification: (1) according to *Group Psychology and the Analysis of the Ego,* there is the identification which precedes all clear, unequivocal, object choice (narcissistic identification); and (2) there is that identification which follows the stage of object formation and leads to the final construction of the ego ideal through renunciation of objects or their incorporation as the superego (*The Ego and the Id*). There is a discrepancy between the theories set forth in *The Ego and the Id* and those in *Group Psychology,* the former presupposing a stage of narcissistic identification as a forerunner to the stage of object choice, and the latter postulating identification as a form of object cathexis. This discrepancy is only a seeming one, since [the processes of] pre- and post-object-libidinal identification are very closely allied. Freud (*Group Psychology*, p. 69) observes, "Identification is the earliest and most primordial form of emotional development," and (in *The Ego and the Id*, p. 36), "However, the object choices pertaining to the first sexual stage and corresponding to the father and mother are, in the normal course of events, apparently incorporated into such identification, and thereby appear *to reinforce the primary identifications.*"

[74]Some time ago, Waelder made a gratifying effort to clarify the theoretical prerequisites for affecting schizophrenia: "Über Mechanismen und Beeinflussungsmöglichkeiten der Psychosen," *Internat. Ztschr. f. PsA.*, X, 1924.

[75]As to current attempts at dealing with this enormous masochistic fixation through a systematic breaking-off of treatment ("weaning by the doctor"), we cannot yet comment on account of insufficient results.

[76]The way in which some intellectually defective impulsives lose their "weakness" after ego integration leads us to conjecture that even intellectual defects may be psychogenic.

[77]The theoretical components of "ego analysis," such as the analysis of identifications, particularly of the superego and narcissism, etc., are even empirically feasible. Yet, at the same time, they are not separable in practice from the analysis of libido transference. Above all, libido transference is also the vehicle of ego analysis.

The Basic Antithesis of Vegetative Life Functions

[1]Cf. my paper on "The Orgasm as an Electrophysiological Discharge," this journal [*Zeitschrift für politische Psychologie und Sexualökonomie*] Vol. I., 1934.

[2]Freud, "Das Ich und das Es," Intern. Psychoanalyt. Press, Vienna.

[3]Cf. Reich: *Der triebhafte Charakter*, Intern. Psychoanalyt. Press, 1925.

[4]"... the question as to what the anxiety consists of, has become of less interest." (Freud, *Neue Folge der Vorlesungen*, p. 115).

[5]"It is not the inhibition that creates the anxiety, but the anxiety is there first, the anxiety is what causes the inhibition." (Freud, *loc cit.*, p. 119).

[6]Cf. My detailed remarks in *Die Funktion des Orgasmus*, 1927.

[7]"Anxiety as the signal of the ego may (also) serve the development of anxiety in the anxiety neurosis through physical damage. That it is the libido itself which is thereby changed into anxiety, we shall no longer maintain." (Freud, *loc cit.*, p. 130).

[8]Many analysts claim that they are unable to confirm my finding that every correct analysis finally reaches a stasis neurosis; yet this fact is undeniable. For many years, I could not understand these objections, until it finally became clear that they involved differences in technique and depended upon whether or not stasis anxiety developed during the course of the analysis. Since most of the affect is bound up in character reactions, one does not get energy in the unbound state if the character analysis remains incomplete.

A follower of my character-analytic technique has compared it to the smashing of the atom; indeed, we get sufficient affect only if we take the character apart via this technique. As a result of differences in technique, large theoretical differences were bound to occur over the years, for the simple reason that the patients' reactions differed according to the approach. For this reason, my formulation of the basic antithesis of sexuality and anxiety, and my reduction of the various secondary drives to anxiety, and of stasis anxiety to free genital streaming, were not duly understood; likewise, the statements of this paper will scarcely be confirmable unless the technique of character analysis is used.

[9]See "The Masochistic Character" in *Charakteranalyse*, 1933.

[10]*Elektrophysiologie der Pflänze*, Springer, 1924.

[11]In the available physiological explanation of anxiety, is there any confirmation of the death instinct hypothesis which currently holds sway in psychoanalytic theory? A supporter of the latter might say the following: if the cumulative effect of the potassium-ion group represents the sexual function, then the calcium effect would represent the death function, the dying-off of the tissue. I would then counter with the same observations I made in my investigation of character, plus one further argument: the potassium-ion concentration makes itself felt as an instinctual drive. The calcium-ion concentration, on the other

hand, is not experienced as a drive, which would correspond to *wanting* to die, but rather is felt as *anxiety*. The death drive is by no means silent or mute, but what is referred to as the death drive, namely the retrogressive movement of life energy, makes itself clearly noticeable as *anxiety*. This idea takes us even a step further. It is true that the calcium group produces phenomena like those seen in a dying person: contraction of the peripheral vessels, pallor, anxiety, trembling, and so on. But these phenomena are only objectively presented, not subjectively willed, like the potassium-ion effects. It is also true that the calcium-ion group shows the effect of promoting and speeding the processes of aging and dying. But we would be mistaken not to see that this is a result of blocking sexual functioning, and that the organism defends itself against the increase of inner tension in the form of anxiety. If, finally, chronic anxiety processes were to hasten dying, this would not prove the existence of the death instinct but only of the life-hostile effect of sexual repression, inasmuch as vagus inhibition promotes sympathetic function, that is, the desiccation, the enervation, the crawling back into oneself—in short, the rejection of all life functions. Thus, we cannot find here arguments in support of the death instinct theory, which represents an apology for the life-negative effect of society and illness.

The Orgasm as an Electrophysiological Discharge

[1]Reich, "Kritik der bürgerlichen Sexualreform," *Geschlechtsreife, Enthaltsamkeit, Ehemoral,* Vienna, Münster Press, 1930, p. 15.

[2]*Zeitschrift für Sexualwissenschaft,* 1923, p. 552.

[3]See my study of the genital character in *Charakteranalyse,* Berlin Sexpol Press, 1933, p. 16.

Experimental Investigation of the Electrical Function of Sexuality and Anxiety

[1][An energy field around all living organisms—from slime moulds to man —was demonstrated experimentally by Dr. H. S. Burr, a Yale neurophysiologist. Such demonstrations had only become possible in the early 1930s with the advent of the vacuum tube triode. Both Reich and Burr (the latter over a period of many years) used an amplifier of this type with high input impedance for the measurement of bioelectric potentials in the living organism. Dr.

Leonard J. Ravitz, employing similar techniques, was able to show in human subjects a high degree of statistical correlation between polarity and intensity of these energy fields and various emotional states. For an excellent bibliography on the electrodynamic field, the reader is referred to Ravitz's article "History, Measurement and Applicability of the Electromagnetic Field in Health and Disease," *Annals of the New York Academy of Sciences*, 98, 1962.—*Trans.*].

[2] One may object that the wandering potential could be the result of local conditions in the electrode. Any phenomenon which might arise from the electrode must be ruled out *in every case*. (Cf. also "Results of control experiments," below).

[3] The results observed here are in agreement with phenomena already known in the field of experimental physics. When two objects of different materials are brought together, an electrical field is generated between their two surfaces just within the boundary layers. For example, we may connect two different objects such as hair and a hand, respectively, to opposite poles of a current meter; if we approximate them carefully so that they are just touching, they will act upon each other at molecular distances, i.e., 10^8 cm. Thus, explain the physicists, the electrons are attracted from one body to the other and become "absorbed" on the surface of the latter. This gives rise to an electrical field with extremely short lines of force within the boundary layers of the two objects. This is called the "double-layer effect," and the voltage so produced is termed the "contact potential." The latter may be anywhere from .001 V to 1 V, as in our results. If the hand is rubbed over the hair, the two objects together constitute a "condenser": the lines of force become more concentrated, and the contact potential increases as the condenser becomes increasingly charged. This is registered on the current meter as a sudden deflection of the needle (i.e., sudden increase in current). Both objects may be insulating materials, or one of them may be a metal; however, both may not be conductors. (From R. W. Pohl, *Elektrizitätslehre*, 1935, p. 196.) These explanations of physics say nothing about how the increased charge on an erogenous skin surface arises.

[4] [The original manuscript fails to give a figure for the initial rise.—*Trans.*]

Bibliographical Abbreviations